PCI
MANUAL FOR THE DESIGN
OF
HOLLOW CORE SLABS

SECOND EDITION

by

Donald R. Buettner and Roger J. Becker
Computerized Structural Design, S.C.

Prepared for the
PCI Hollow Core Slab Producers
Committee

John E. Saccoman, Chairperson

James Beerbower	**Ernest Markle**
Kevin Boyle	**James Markle**
Jeffrey Butler	**Milo J. Nimmer**
Loris Collavino	**William C. Richardson, Jr.**
Edward J. Gregory	**Klaus Rosenstern**
Pat Hynes	**Wes Schrooten**
Paul Kourajian	**Larry Stigler**

PRECAST/PRESTRESSED
CONCRETE INSTITUTE

209 W. Jackson Blvd.
Chicago, Illinois 60606
Phone: 312-786-0300
Fax: 312-786-0353
info@pci.org

ISBN 0–937040–57–6

Printed in U.S.A.

INTRODUCTION

Purpose of Manual

The application and design of precast, prestressed hollow core slabs is similar to that of other prestressed members. However, there are situations which are unique to hollow core slabs either because of the way the slabs are produced or because of the application of the slabs.

For special situations, hollow core producers have developed design criteria and conducted in-house testing to verify that their approaches are valid. In fact, there is consistency between the many types of hollow core slabs available. The purpose of this manual is to bring together those things that are common, that are verified by test and that can be universally applied to hollow core slabs. Because there are differences, some topics covered will also point to the differences where closer coordination with the local producer is required.

This manual was prepared by Computerized Structural Design, S.C., Milwaukee, Wisconsin with input and direction from the PCI Hollow Core Slab Producers Committee. Additionally, the fire and acoustical sections were prepared by Armand Gustaferro of The Consulting Engineers Group, Inc., Mt. Prospect, Illinois and Allen H. Shiner of Shiner and Associates, Inc., Skokie, Illinois, respectively. All reasonable care has been used to verify the accuracy of material contained in this manual. However, the manual should be used only by those experienced in structural design and should not replace good structural engineering judgment.

Scope of Manual

This document is intended to cover the primary design requirements for hollow core floor and roof systems. In instances where the design is no different than for other prestressed members, the PCI Design Handbook and the ACI Building Code should be consulted for more in-depth discussion.

For the architect or consulting engineer, this manual is intended as a guideline for working with hollow core slabs, a guide for the use and application of hollow core slabs and an indication of some of the limitations of hollow core slabs. For the plant engineer, the manual will hopefully present some backup and reference material for dealing with everyday design problems.

TABLE OF CONTENTS

Introduction

Notation

NOTATION

A = Cross-sectional area

a = Depth of equivalent compression stress block

a_θ = Depth of equivalent compression stress block under fire conditions

A_{cr} = Area of crack face

A_e = Net effective slab bearing area

A_{ps} = Area of prestressed reinforcement

A_{vf} = Area of shear friction reinforcement

b = Width of compression face

b_w = Net web width of hollow core slab

C = Confinement factor

C = Compressive force

C = Seismic factor dependent on site and structure fundamental period

C = Factor for calculating steel relaxation losses as given in Table 2.2.3.2

c = Distance from extreme compression fiber to neutral axis

CR = Prestress loss due to concrete creep

C_s = Seismic coefficient

D = Dead load

d = Distance from extreme compression fiber to centroid of non-prestressed tension reinforcement

d_b = Nominal diameter of reinforcement

d_p = Distance from extreme compression fiber to centroid of prestressed reinforcement

DW = Distribution width

e = Distance from neutral axis to centroid of prestressed reinforcement

E_c = Modulus of elasticity of concrete

E_{ci} = Modulus of elasticity of concrete at the time of initial prestress

ES = Prestress loss due to elastic shortening of concrete

E_s = Modulus of elasticity of steel reinforcement

f'_c = Specified design compressive strength of concrete

f'_{ci} = Compressive strength of concrete at the time of initial prestress

f_{cir} = Net compressive stress in concrete at centroid of prestressed reinforcement at time of initial prestress

f_{cds} = Stress in concrete at centroid of prestressed reinforcement due to superimposed dead load

f_d = Stress at extreme tension fiber due to unfactored member self weight

F_i = Portion of base shear applied at level i

f_{pc} = Compressive stress in concrete at the centroid of the section due to effective prestress for non-composite sections or due to effective prestress and moments resisted by the precast section alone for composite sections

f_{pe} = Compressive stress in concrete at extreme fiber where external loads cause tension due to the effective prestress only

f_{ps} = Stress in prestressed reinforcement at nominal strength

$f_{ps\theta}$ = Stress in prestressed reinforcement at fire strength

f'_{ps} = Maximum steel stress in partially developed strand

f_{pu} = Specified tensile strength of prestressing steel

$f_{pu\theta}$ = Tensile strength of prestressing steel at elevated temperatures

F_{px} = Force applied to diaphragm at level under consideration

f_{se} = Effective stress in prestressing steel after all losses

f_{si} = Stress in prestressing steel at initial prestress

F_t = Additional portion of base shear applied at top level

f_u = Usable grout strength in a horizontal joint

f_y = Steel yield strength

h = Overall member depth

h_n = Net height of grout in keyway between slab units

I = Occupancy importance factor

I = Cross-sectional moment of inertia

J = Factor for calculating steel relaxation losses as given in Table 2.2.3.1

k = Fraction of total load in a horizontal joint in a grout column

K_{cir} = Factor for calculating elastic shortening prestress losses

K_{cr} = Factor for calculating prestress losses due to concrete creep

K_{es} = Factor for calculating prestress losses due to elastic shortening

K_{re} = Factor for calculating prestress losses due to steel relaxation as given in Table 2.2.3.1

K_{sh}	=	Factor for calculating prestress losses due to concrete shrinkage
K'_u	=	Factor from PCI Handbook Fig. 4.12.2 for calculating flexural design strength
L	=	Live load
ℓ	=	Span length
ℓ_d	=	Reinforcement development length
ℓ_e	=	Strand embedment length from member end to point of maximum stress
ℓ_f	=	Flexural bond length
ℓ_t	=	Strand transfer length
M	=	Service load moment
M_{cr}	=	Cracking moment
M_d	=	Unfactored dead load moment
M_g	=	Unfactored self-weight moment
M_n	=	Nominal flexural strength
$M_{n\theta}$	=	Flexural strength under fire conditions
M_{max}	=	Maximum factored moment due to externally applied loads
	=	$M_u - M_d$
M_{sd}	=	Unfactored moment due to superimposed dead load
M_u	=	Factored design moment
M_θ	=	Applied fire moment
P	=	Effective force in prestressing steel after all losses
P_o	=	Effective prestress force at release prior to long term losses
P_i	=	Initial prestress force after seating losses
Q	=	First moment of area
R	=	Fire endurance rating
RE	=	Prestress loss due to steel relaxation
R_e	=	Reduction factor for load eccentricity in horizontal joints
RH	=	Ambient relative humidity
R_w	=	Seismic coefficient dependent on structural system type
S	=	Section modulus
SH	=	Prestress loss due to concrete shrinkage
T	=	Tensile force
t_g	=	Width of grout column in horizontal joint
V	=	Seismic base shear
V_c	=	Nominal shear strength of concrete
V_{ci}	=	Nominal shear strength of concrete in a shear-flexure failure mode
V_{cw}	=	Nominal shear strength of concrete in a web shear failure mode
V_d	=	Shear due to unfactored self weight
V_h	=	Horizontal beam shear

V_i	=	Factored shear force due to externally applied loads occurring simultaneously with M_{max}
	=	$V_u - V_d$
V_n	=	Nominal shear strength of a member
V_s	=	Nominal shear strength provided by shear reinforcement
V_u	=	Design shear force
V/S	=	Volume to surface ratio
w	=	Uniformly distributed load
w	=	Bearing area length
W	=	Total dead load plus other applicable loads for seismic design
w_i	=	Portion of W at level i
w_{px}	=	Portion of W at level under consideration
y_b	=	Distance from neutral axis to extreme bottom fiber
y_t	=	Used as either distance to top fiber or tension fiber from neutral axis
Z	=	Seismic zone factor
β_1	=	Factor defined in ACI 318-95, Section 10.2.7.3
γ_p	=	Factor for type of prestressing strand
δ_{all}	=	Limiting free end slip
δ_s	=	Actual free end slip
ε_{ps}	=	Strain in prestressed reinforcement at nominal flexural strength
ε_s	=	Strain in prestressed reinforcement
ε_{se}	=	Strain in prestressed reinforcement after losses
μ	=	Shear friction coefficient
μ_e	=	Effective shear friction coefficient
ρ_p	=	Ratio of prestressed reinforcement
ρ'	=	Ratio of compression reinforcement
ϕ	=	ACI strength reduction factor
ω	=	$\rho f_y / f'_c$
ω'	=	$\rho' f_y / f'_c$
ω_p	=	$\rho_p f_{ps} / f'_c$
ω_w	=	Reinforcement index for flanged sections
ω'_w	=	Reinforcement index for flanged sections
ω_{pw}	=	Reinforcement index for flanged sections
ω_{pu}	=	$\rho_p f_{pu} / f'_c$
θ	=	Subscript denoting fire conditions

CHAPTER 1

HOLLOW CORE SLAB SYSTEMS

1.1 Methods of Manufacturing

A hollow core slab is a precast, prestressed concrete member with continuous voids provided to reduce weight and, therefore, cost and, as a side benefit, to use for concealed electrical or mechanical runs. Primarily used as floor or roof deck systems, hollow core slabs also have applications as wall panels, spandrel members and bridge deck units.

An understanding of the methods used to manufacture hollow core slabs will aid in the special considerations sometimes required in the use of hollow core slabs. Hollow core slabs are cast using various methods in the seven major systems available today. Because each production system is patented, producers are usually set up on a franchise or license basis using the background, knowledge and expertise provided with the machine development. Each producer then has the technical support of a large network of associated producers.

Two basic manufacturing methods are currently in use for the production of hollow core slabs. One is a dry cast or extrusion system where a very low slump concrete is forced through the machine. The cores are formed with augers or tubes with the concrete being compacted around the cores. The second system uses a higher slump concrete. Sides are formed either with stationary, fixed forms or with forms attached to the machine with the sides being slip formed. The cores in the normal slump, or wet cast, systems are formed with either lightweight aggregate fed through tubes attached to the casting machine, pneumatic tubes anchored in a fixed form or long tubes attached to the casting machine which slip form the cores.

Table 1.1 lists the seven major hollow core systems available today along with the basic information on the casting technique. Various names may be used by local licensees to describe the same products. In most cases, the slabs are cast on long line beds, normally 300 ft to 600 ft long. Slabs are then sawcut to the appropriate length for the intended project.

The economy of the generalized hollow core system is in the quantity of slabs that can be produced at a given time with a minimum of labor required. Each slab on a given casting line will have the same number of prestressing strands. Therefore, the greatest production efficiency is obtained by mixing slabs with the same reinforcing requirements from several projects on a single production line. This implies that best efficiency for a single project is obtained if slab requirements are repetitive.

1.2 Materials

As stated previously, hollow core slabs are produced with two basic concrete mixes; low slump and normal slump concrete. For the low slump concretes, water content is limited to slightly more than that required for cement hydration. Water-cement ratios are typically about 0.3. Mixing is critical because the limited water available must be well dispersed in the mix. Water reducing admixtures can be used to optimize a mix by reducing cement and water requirements while still retaining adequate workability for proper compaction of the concrete by the machine. Air entrainment admixtures are not effective in the dry mix concrete. With the low water-cement ratios and compaction placing method, air is difficult to disperse well and maintain.

Table 1.1 Hollow Core Systems

Manufac-turer	Machine Type	Concrete Type/Slump	Core Form
Dy-Core	Extruder	Dry/Low	Tubes
Dynaspan	Slip Form	Wet/Normal	Tubes
Elematic	Extruder	Dry/Low	Auger/Tube
Flexicore	Fixed Form	Wet/Normal	Pneumatic Tubes
Spancrete	Slip Form	Dry/Low	Tubes
SpanDeck	Slip Form	Wet/Normal	Filler aggregate
Ultra-Span	Extruder	Dry/Low	Augers

Latex feathering ready for direct carpet application

Acoustical spray on exposed slab ceiling

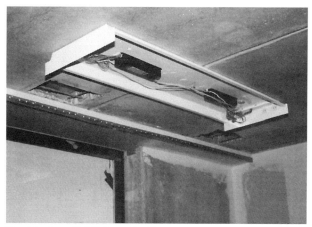

Electrical and HVAC application

The wet cast products (those cast with normal slump concrete), have water-cement ratios in the range of 0.4 to 0.45. Depending on the slip forming system used, slumps of 2 to 5 inches (50 - 130 mm) are used. The mix design and use of admixtures is dependent on achieving a mix that will hold its shape consistent with the forming technique used.

Aggregates vary in the various manufacturing processes depending on what type is locally available. Maximum aggregate size larger than pea gravel is rarely used because of the confined areas into which concrete must be placed. Light weight aggregates are occasionally used to reduce the weight of the sections and to achieve a significant reduction in required equivalent thickness in a fire rated application. Concrete unit weights ranging from 110 to 150 pcf (1760 - 2400 kg/m^3) are used in the industry.

Strand use in hollow core slabs includes about every size and type of strand produced depending on what is available to a particular producer. The trend is toward primary use of the larger $^1/_2$ in (13 mm) diameter, low relaxation strand. The philosophy of strand use varies from using many strand sizes to optimize cost for a given project to using only one or two strand sizes for simplicity of inventory and production.

Except for special situations, keyway grout is normally a sand and Portland cement mixture in proportions of about 3:1. The amount of water used is a function of the method used to place the grout but will generally result in a wet mix so keyways may be easily filled. Shrinkage cracks may occur in the keyways, but configuration of the key is such that vertical load transfer can still occur with the presence of a shrinkage crack. Rarely is grout strength required in excess of 2000 psi (13.8 MPa) for vertical load transfer.

Although it is discouraged, non-shrink, non-staining grout is occasionally specified for use in keyways. In evaluating the potential benefits of non-shrink grout, the volume of grout must be compared to the overall volume of concrete in the slabs and support materials. Because the size of the keyway is small in relation to a floor or roof assembly of slabs, total shrinkage will be affected only to a minor degree. Shrinkage cracks can still occur in the keyways and there is little benefit to be gained in comparison with the additional cost.

1.3 Advantages of Hollow Core Slabs

Hollow core slabs are most widely known for providing economical, efficient floor and roof systems. The top surface can be prepared for the installation of a floor covering by feathering the joints with a latex cement, installing non-structural fill concretes ranging from $1/2$ in to 2 in (13 - 51 mm) thick depending on the material used, or by casting a composite structural concrete topping. The underside can be used as a finished ceiling as installed, by painting, or by applying an acoustical spray.

When properly coordinated for alignment, the voids in a hollow core slab may be used for electrical or mechanical runs. For example, routing of a lighting circuit through the cores can allow fixtures in an exposed slab ceiling without unsightly surface mounted conduit. Slabs used as the heated mass in a passive solar application can be detailed to distribute the heated air through the cores.

Structurally, a hollow core slab provides the efficiency of a prestressed member for load capacity, span range, and deflection control. In addition, a basic diaphragm is provided for resisting lateral loads by the grouted slab assembly provided proper connections and details exist. A detailed discussion of diaphragm capabilities is presented in Chapter 4.

Excellent fire resistance is another attribute of the hollow core slab. Depending on thickness and strand cover, ratings up to a 4 hour endurance can be achieved. A fire rating is dependent on equivalent thickness for heat transmission, concrete cover over the prestressing strands for strength in a high temperature condition, and end restraint. Underwriters Laboratories publishes fire ratings for various assemblies. However, many building codes allow a rational design procedure for strength in a fire. This procedure, described in detail in Chapter 6, considers strand temperature in calculating strength. Required fire ratings should be clearly specified in the contract documents. Also, the fire rating should be considered in determining the slab thickness to be used in preliminary design.

Used as floor-ceiling assemblies, hollow core slabs have the excellent sound transmission characteristics associated with concrete. The Sound Transmission Class rating ranges from about 47 to 57 without topping and the Impact Insulation Class rating starts at about 23 for a plain slab and may be increased to over 70 with the addition of carpeting and padding. Detailed information on the acoustical properties of hollow core slabs is presented in Chapter 7.

1.4 Framing Concepts

The primary consideration in developing a framing scheme using hollow core slabs is the span length. For a given loading and fire endurance rating, span length and slab thickness may be optimized by consulting a producer's published load tables. Section 1.7 presents sample load tables and instructions for the use of the tables. The PCI Design Handbook[1] recommends limits on span-depth ratios for the hollow core slabs. For roof slabs, a span-depth ratio limit of 50 is suggested and for floor slabs, a limit of 40 is suggested. In practice, a span-depth ratio of 45 is common for floors and roofs when fire endurance, openings, or heavy or sustained live loads do not control a design.

Consideration must be given to factors which affect slab thickness selection for a given span. Heavy superimposed loads, as required by the function of a system, would require a lower span-depth ratio. Similarly, heavy partitions or a large number of openings will result in higher load capacity requirements. The fire resistance rating required for the application will also affect the load capacity of a slab. As the code required fire rating increases, prestressing strands can be raised for more protection from the heat. The smaller effective strand depth will result in a lower load capacity. Alternatively, a rational design procedure can be used to consider the elevated strand temperatures during a fire. This fire design condition may control a slab design and, again, result in a lower load capacity.

Once slab thicknesses and spans are selected, the economics of layout become important. While ends cut at an angle can be designed and supplied, it is most efficient to have the bearing perpendicular to the span so square cut ends can be used.

It is also desirable to have the plan dimensions fit the slab module. This is dependent upon the slab systems available in the project area. Non-module plan dimensions can be accommodated using partial width slabs. Some producers intentionally cast narrow widths as filler pieces while others use a section split from a full slab. Such a split section might be created by a longitudinal sawcut or a break if the edge will not be exposed to view.

Construction tolerances must be accounted for in developing a plan layout. Tolerance on slab length may be taken up by allowing a gap at the slab ends in the bearing detail. On the non-bearing sides, clearance may be provided by using a detail where the slabs lap over a wall or beam. If the slab edge butts a wall or beam, a gap should be provided. Refer to local producers' information for recommendations of proper tolerances.

When a hollow core slab deck is exposed to weather for a long period of time during construction, water can accumulate in the cores. The primary source of water infiltration is at the butt joints. In cold weather, this water can freeze and expand causing localized damage. One remedy for this situation is to drill weep holes at the slab ends under each core. The need for such weep holes is generally known only after a construction schedule is established. The specifier and the slab supplier are not usually in a position to know of such a need in advance.

Hollow core members will be cambered as with any other prestressed flexural member. In the planning stages, consideration should be given to the causes of differential camber. For two slabs of identical length and prestressing, the camber may be different because of concrete and curing variations. This factor is independent of a framing scheme. However, joints between slabs of unequal spans or joints at which a change in the span direction occurs, will cause a potential differential camber problem. This must be recognized and dealt with in the design layout. Wall locations may hide such a joint, but the door swing might be directed to the least variable side.

Camber must also be accommodated when a topping is to be provided. The quantity of topping required must consider the amount of camber and the function of the floor. In occupancies where flat floors are not a requirement, a constant topping thickness may be used to follow the curvature of the slabs. At the other extreme, if a "flat" floor is required in a structure consisting of multiple bays of varying length and change in slab direction, the highest point will determine the top elevation of the topping. A greater amount of topping will then be required in "low" areas. These considerations must be dealt with in the planning stages to both control costs and minimize questions and potential for "extras" during construction.

Camber, camber growth, and deflections must be considered when slabs run parallel to a stiff vertical element such as a wall (e.g. slabs running parallel to the front wall of an elevator). The door rough opening should allow for camber to produce proper door installation. Alternatively, the slab span might be rearranged so the front wall is a bearing wall. Then door problems would be alleviated.

Camber, camber growth, and deflections must be taken into account in roofing details. Where changes in relative slab position can occur, counterflashings are suggested to accommodate such changes.

1.5 Wall Panel Applications

Some hollow core slab systems can also provide slabs to be used as walls. Long line manufacturing can result in economical cladding or load bearing panels used in manufacturing or commercial applications. The hollow core wall panels are prestressed with two layers of strands for accommodating handling, structural loadings and bowing considerations. Some manufacturers can add 2 in to 4 in (51 - 102 mm) of insulation to the hollow core section with a 1 $1/2$ in thick to 3 in (38 - 76 mm) thick concrete facing to create an insulated sandwich panel.

A variety of architectural finishes are available with hollow core wall panels. While the finishes can be very good, the variety of finishes available is different from those typically available with true architectural precast concrete panels. In judging the quality of finish on hollow core wall panels, consideration must be given to the manufacturing process.

1.6 Design Responsibilities

It is customary in the hollow core industry for the producer to perform the final engineering for the product to be supplied to the job. This would include design for vertical loads and lateral loads specified by the Engineer of Record, embedded items for specified connection forces, and handling and shipping. However, the Engineer of Record plays a very important role in the design process. Prior to selection of the hollow core producer, enough preliminary planning should be done to insure that the specified floor and roof system is achievable. That is, the project should be one that can be engineered without requiring changes from the contract documents.

The contract documents must clearly indicate design criteria to which hollow core slabs will have to conform. This is especially important when the hollow core slabs must interface with other construction materials. When connections are required, the forces to be transmitted through the connections must be specified in the contract documents. The producer is best able to determine the most efficient connection element to be embedded in the slab. However, the balance of a connection which interfaces with another material should be detailed in the contract documents.

The Engineer of Record also has a responsibility in the review and approval of erection drawings prepared by the precast producer. Review of these drawings is the last opportunity to assure that the producer's understanding of the project coincides with the intent of design. Erection drawings should be checked for proper design loads, proper details and bearing conditions, conformance with specified fire ratings, and the location of openings.

1.7 Cross-Sections and Load Tables

Each of the major hollow core slab systems has a standard set of cross-sections that can be produced by their equipment. Available in thicknesses ranging from 4 in to 15 in (102 - 380 mm), core configurations make each system unique. Each individual producer has additional production practices which may affect the capabilities of their product. Therefore, most producers prepare and distribute load tables in their market area.

Producer load tables define the allowable live load that a given slab can safely support in addition to the slab self weight. The load capacity will be a function of the slab thickness, the amount of prestressing provided, and the location of the prestressing strands. Fire rated slabs may require additional concrete cover below the strands which will affect the load capacity.

The design criteria used to develop these load tables is defined by the ACI Building Code[2] as outlined in Chapter 2. Depending on the design criteria controlling a slab's load capacity, some advantage may be gained by understanding that in most applications, superimposed loads will consist of both dead and live loads. Where ultimate strength controls, an equivalent live load can be used to enter a load table. It is calculated as:

$$w_{equivalent} = \frac{1.4}{1.7} \text{ superimposed Dead load} + \text{Live load}$$

However, if bottom fiber tensile stresses control, no adjustment in superimposed loads may be used.

Similarly, many loading conditions consist of loads other than uniform loads. For preliminary design only, an equivalent uniform load may be calculated from the maximum moment caused by the actual loads.

$$w_{equivalent} = \frac{8 \, M_{superimposed}}{\ell^2}$$

Shear will not be properly addressed in this situation. Thus, the final design must consider the actual load pattern.

Because of the uniqueness of each hollow core slab system and the many possibilities of strand patterns available from various producers, a generic hollow core slab has been developed to demonstrate design procedures. Figure 1.7.1 depicts the slab section and properties and illustrates a typical form for a producer's load tables. Throughout this manual, this section will be used to demonstrate various calculation procedures where any one of the proprietary cross-sections could be substituted. *It must be emphasized that this cross-section is not available for use and should not be specified.*

Figures 1.7.2 through 1.7.8 present the proprietary slab cross-sections currently available. The section properties are as provided by the manufacturers, but weights are based on 150 pcf (2400 kg/m^3) concrete. The actual weights may vary slightly from those given. The availability of any particular section in a given area must be verified with the local producers. Figures 1.7.9 present charts of the general range of load capacities available in a given slab thickness. As with any chart of this nature, the chart should be carefully approached and verified with local producer load tables, especially for the longest and shortest and lightest and heaviest conditions. Special care is also required when fire rated slabs must be used on a project. (See Chapter 6)

The following examples demonstrate the ways in which load tables may be used.

Example 1.7.1 Equivalent Uniform Load

From the load table in Figure 1.7.1 select a strand pattern to carry a uniform superimposed dead load of 20 psf and a uniform live load of 60 psf on a 24 foot span.

$w_{total} = 20 + 60 = 80$ psf

4-7/16 in dia. strands required: capacity = 118 psf flexural strength controls

$$w_{equivalent} = \frac{1.4}{1.7}(20) + 60 = 77 \text{ psf}$$

Use 4-3/8 in dia. strands: capacity = 79 psf flexural strength controls.

Example 1.7.2 Non-Uniform Loads

From the load table in Figure 1.7.1 select a strand pattern to carry a superimposed uniform load of 20 psf dead plus 40 psf live and a continuous wall load of 600 plf located perpendicular to the span and at midspan. The design span is 25 feet.

For preliminary design

$$M_{superimposed} = \frac{25^2}{8}(20 + 40) + \frac{25}{4}(600)$$

$$= 8438 \text{ ft-\#/ft}$$

$$w_{equivalent} = \frac{8(8438)}{25^2}$$

$$= 108 \text{ psf}$$

Try 6-3/8 in dia. strands - capacity = 120 psf

For final design use the methods of Chapter 2 particularly to check shear.

1.8 Tolerances[3]

Figure 1.8.1 shows the dimensional tolerances for precast hollow core slabs. These tolerances are guidelines only and each project must be considered individually to ensure that the tolerances shown are applicable.

Figure 1.8.2 shows erection tolerances for hollow core slabs. When establishing tolerances, the function of the slabs should be considered. For example, slabs covered by finish materials may not need the close tolerances required for exposed slabs.

Fig. 1.7.1 Generic hollow core slab

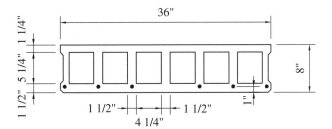

Section Properties
A = 154 in^2
I = 1224.5 in^4
b_w = 10.5 in
y_b = 3.89 in
S_b = 314.8 in^3
S_t = 297.9 in^3
wt = 53.5 psf

SAMPLE LOAD TABLE[3]

Allowable Superimposed Live Loads, psf

Strands, 270LR	ϕMn, ft-k	Spans, ft									
		14	15	16	17	18	19	20	21	22	23
4-3/8″	45.1	317	270	232	200	174	152	133	116	102	90
6-3/8″	65.4			356	311	272	240	212	188	168	150
4-7/16″	59.4			320	278	243	214	189	167	148	132
6-7/16″	85.0					343[1]	311[1]	283[1]	258	231	208
4-1/2″	76.7					327	289	257	229	204	183
6-1/2″	105.3							317[1]	290[1]	267[1]	247[1]

Strands, 270LR	ϕMn, ft-k	24	25	26	27	28	29	30
4-3/8″	45.1	79	79	69	61	53	46	
6-3/8″	65.4	134	120	108	97	87	78	70
4-7/16″	59.4	118	105	94	84	75	67	59
6-7/16″	85.0	187	169	153	139	126	114	104
4-1/2″	76.7	165	148	134	121	109	99	90
6-1/2″	105.3	227[1]	210[1]	195[2]	178[2]	163[2]	149[2]	137[2]

1 - Values are governed by shear strength.
2 - Values are governed by allowable tension
3 - Table based on 5000 psi concrete with $6\sqrt{f'_c}$ allowable tension. Unless noted, values are governed by strength design.

Note: *This slab is for illustration purposes only. Do not specify this slab for a project.*

Fig. 1.7.2

Trade name: Dy-Core
Equipment Manufacturer: Mixer Systems, Inc., Pewaukee, Wisconsin

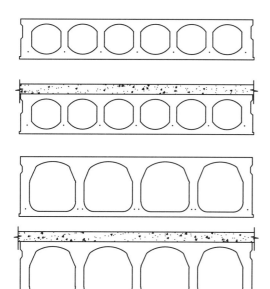

Section	Untopped				with 2″ topping		
width x depth	A in²	y_b in	I in⁴	wt psf	y_b in	I in⁴	wt psf
4′-0″ x 6″	142	3.05	661	37	4.45	1475	62
4′-0″ x 8″	193	3.97	1581	50	5.43	3017	75
4′-0″ x 10″	215	5.40	2783	56	6.89	4614	81
4′-0″ x 12″	264	6.37	4773	69	7.89	7313	94
4′-0″ x 15″	289	7.37	8604	76	9.21	13225	101

Note: All sections not available from all producers. Check availability with local manufacturers.

Fig. 1.7.3

Trade name: Dynaspan®
Equipment Manufacturer: Dynamold Corporation, Salina, Kansas

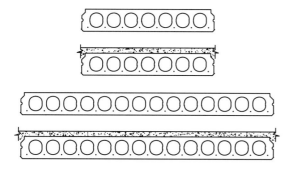

Section	Untopped				with 2″ topping		
width x depth	A in²	y_b in	I in⁴	wt psf	y_b in	I in⁴	wt psf
4′-0″ x 4″	133	2.00	235	35	3.08	689	60
4′-0″ x 6″	165	3.02	706	43	4.25	1543	68
4′-0″ x 8″	233	3.93	1731	61	5.16	3205	86
4′-0″ x 10″	260	4.91	3145	68	6.26	5314	93
8′-0″ x 6″	338	3.05	1445	44	4.26	3106	69
8′-0″ x 8″	470	3.96	3525	61	5.17	6444	86
8′-0″ x 10″	532	4.96	6422	69	6.28	10712	94
8′-0″ x 12″	615	5.95	10505	80	7.32	16507	105

Note: All sections not available from all producers. Check availability with local manufacturers.

Fig. 1.7.4

Trade name: Elematic®
Equipment Manufacturer: Mixer Systems, Inc., Pewaukee, Wisconsin

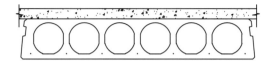
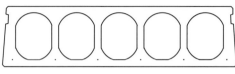
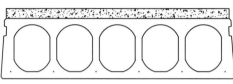

Section	Untopped				with 2″ topping		
width x depth	A in²	y_b in	I in⁴	wt psf	y_b in	I in⁴	wt psf
4′-0″ x 6″	157	3.00	694	41	4.33	1557	66
4′-0″ x 8″	196	3.97	1580	51	5.41	3024	76
4′-0″ x 10″(5)	238	5.00	3042	62	6.49	5190	87
4′-0″ x 10″(6)	249	5.00	3108	65	6.44	5280	90
4′-0″ x 12″	274	6.00	5121	71	7.56	8134	96

Note: Elematic is also availble in 96″ width. All sections not available from all producers. Check availability with local manufacturers.

Fig. 1.7.5

Trade name: Flexicore®
Licensing Organization: The Flexicore Co. Inc., Dayton, Ohio

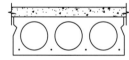
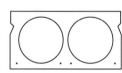
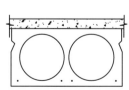

Section	Untopped				with 2″ topping		
width x depth	A in²	y_b in	I in⁴	wt psf	y_b in	I in⁴	wt psf
1′-4″ x 6″	55	3.00	243	43	4.23	523	68
2′-0″ x 6″	86	3.00	366	45	4.20	793	70
1′-4″ x 8″	73	4.00	560	57	5.26	1028	82
2′-0″ x 8″	110	4.00	843	57	5.26	1547	82
1′-8″ x 10″	98	5.00	1254	61	6.43	2109	86
2′-0″ x 10″	138	5.00	1587	72	6.27	2651	97
2′-0″ x 12″	141	6.00	2595	73	7.46	4049	98

Note: All sections not available from all producers. Check availability with local manufacturers.

Fig. 1.7.6

Trade name: Spancrete®
Licensing Organization: Spancrete Machinery Corp., Milwaukee, Wisconsin

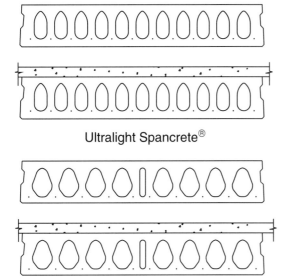

Ultralight Spancrete®

Section	Untopped				with 2″ topping		
width x depth	A in²	y_b in	I in⁴	wt psf	y_b in	I in⁴	wt psf
4′-0″ x 4″	138	2.00	238	34	3.14	739	59
4′-0″ x 6″	189	2.93	762	46	4.19	1760	71
4′-0″ x 8″	258	3.98	1806	63	5.22	3443	88
4′-0″ x 10″	312	5.16	3484	76	6.41	5787	101
4′-0″ x 12″	355	6.28	5784	86	7.58	8904	111
4′-0″ x 15″	370	7.87	9765	90	9.39	14351	115

4′-0″ x 8″	246	4.17	1730	60	5.41	3230	85
4′-0″ x 10″	277	5.22	3178	67	6.58	5376	92
4′-0″ x 12″	316	6.22	5311	77	7.66	8410	102

Note: Spancrete is also available in 40″ and 96″ widths. All sections are not available from all producers. Check availability with local manufacturer.

Fig. 1.7.7

Trade name: SpanDeck®
Licensing Organization: Fabcon, Incorporated, Savage, Minnesota

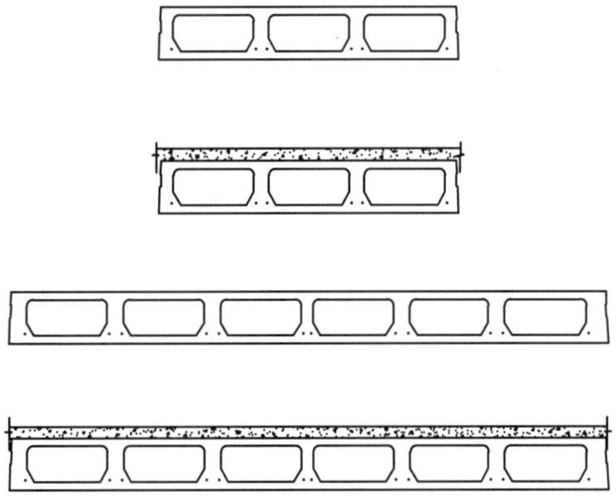

Section	Untopped				with 2″ topping		
width x depth	A in²	y_b in	I in⁴	wt psf	y_b in	I in⁴	wt psf
4′-0″ x 8″	246	3.75	1615	62	5.55	2791	87
4′-0″ x 12″	298	5.87	5452	75	8.01	7856	100
8′-0″ x 8″	477	3.73	3236	60	5.53	5643	85
8′-0″ x 12″	578	5.86	10909	72	7.98	15709	97

Note: All sections not available from all producers. Check availability with local manufacturers.

Fig. 1.7.8

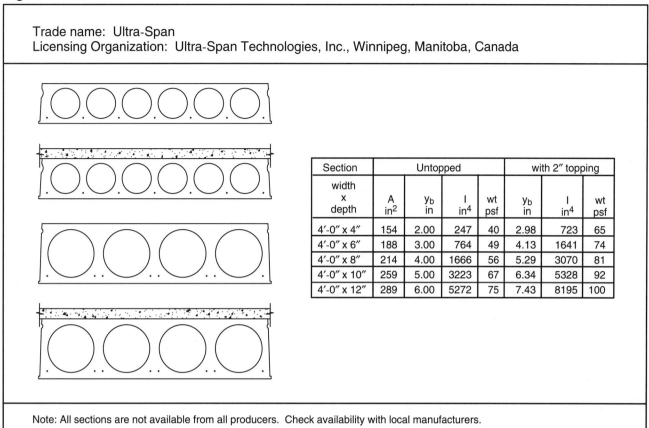

Trade name: Ultra-Span
Licensing Organization: Ultra-Span Technologies, Inc., Winnipeg, Manitoba, Canada

Section	Untopped				with 2″ topping		
width x depth	A in²	y_b in	I in⁴	wt psf	y_b in	I in⁴	wt psf
4'-0″ x 4″	154	2.00	247	40	2.98	723	65
4'-0″ x 6″	188	3.00	764	49	4.13	1641	74
4'-0″ x 8″	214	4.00	1666	56	5.29	3070	81
4'-0″ x 10″	259	5.00	3223	67	6.34	5328	92
4'-0″ x 12″	289	6.00	5272	75	7.43	8195	100

Note: All sections are not available from all producers. Check availability with local manufacturers.

Fig. 1.7.9(a) Slab load ranges

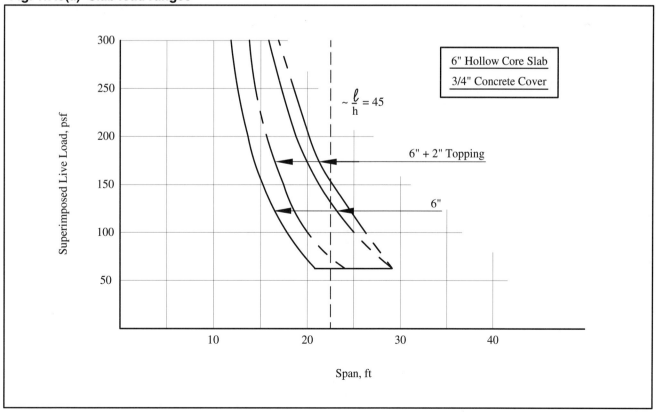

Fig. 1.7.9 (b) Slab load ranges

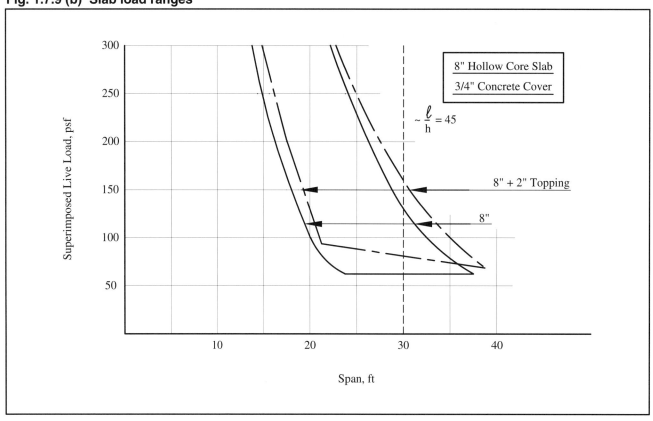

Fig. 1.7.9(c) Slab load ranges

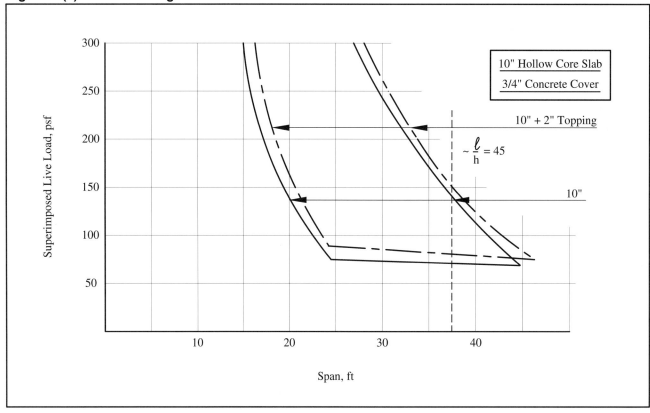

Fig. 1.7.9 (d) Slab load ranges

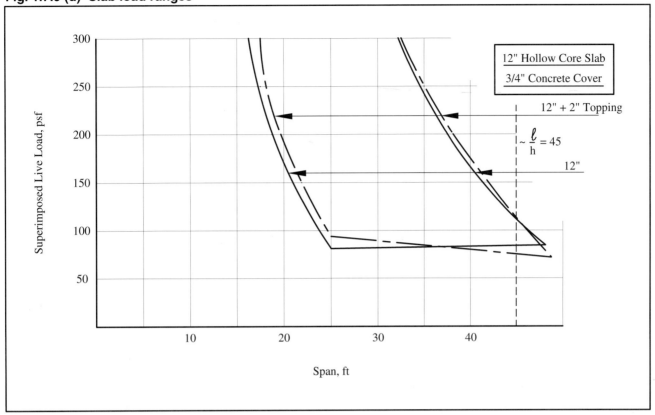

Fig. 1.7.9(e) Slab load ranges

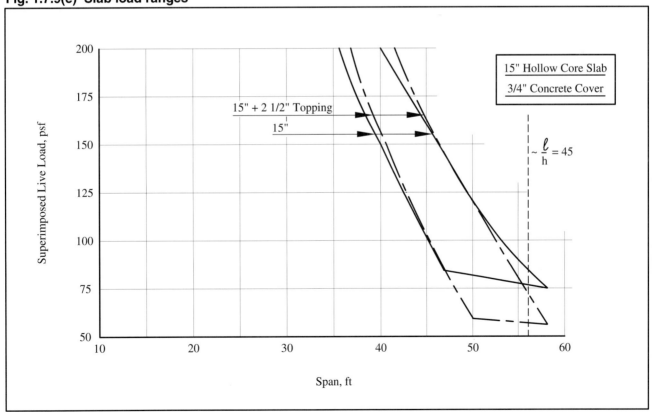

Fig. 1.8.1 Product tolerances – hollow core slabs

a = Length .... ±$\frac{1}{2}$ in
b = Width .... ±$\frac{1}{4}$ in
c = Depth .... ±$\frac{1}{4}$ in
d_t = Top flange thickness
Top flange area defined by the actual measured values of average d_t x b shall not be less than 85% of the nominal area calculated by d_t nominal x b nominal.
d_b = Bottom flange thickness
Bottom flange area defined by the actual measured values of average d_b x b shall not be less than 85% of the nominal area calculated by d_b nominal x b nominal.
e = Web thickness
The total cumulative web thickness defined by the actual measured value Σe shall not be less than 85% of the nominal cumulative width calculated by Σe nominal.
f = Blockout location .... ±2 in
g = Flange angle .... $\frac{1}{8}$ in per 12 in, $\frac{1}{2}$ in max.
h = Variation from specified end squareness
or skew .... ±$\frac{1}{2}$ in
i = Sweep (variation from straight line parallel to centerline of member) .... ±$\frac{3}{8}$ in

j = Center of gravity of strand group
The CG of the strand group relative to the top of the plank shall be within ±$\frac{1}{4}$ in of the nominal strand group CG. The position of any individual strand shall be within ±$\frac{1}{2}$ in of nominal vertical position and ±$\frac{3}{4}$ in of nominal horizontal position and shall have a minimum cover of $\frac{3}{4}$ in.
k = Position of plates .... ±2 in
l = Tipping and flushness of plates .... ±$\frac{1}{4}$ in
m = Local smoothness .... ±$\frac{1}{4}$ in in 10 ft
(does not apply to top deck surface left rough to receive a topping or to visually concealed surfaces)
Plank weight
Excess concrete material in the plank internal features is within tolerance as long as the measured weight of the individual plank does not exceed 110% of the nominal published unit weight used in the load capacity calculation.
n = Applications requiring close control of differential camber between adjacent members of the same design should be discussed in detail with the producer to determine applicable tolerances.

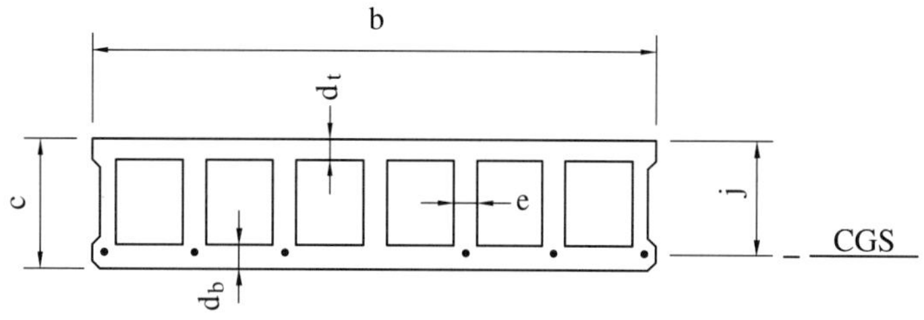

CROSS SECTION

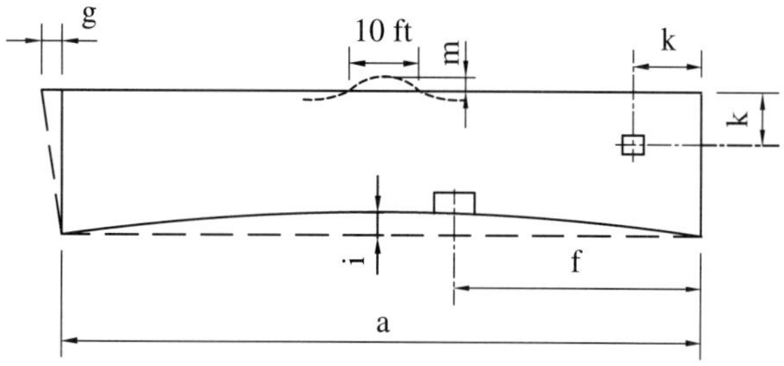

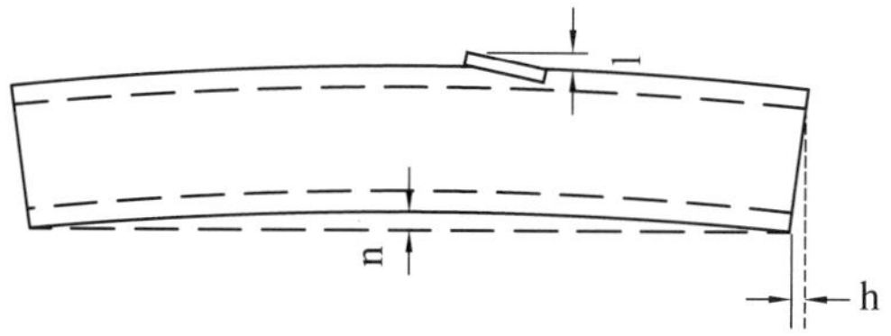

ELEVATION

PLAN

Fig. 1.8.2 Erection tolerances - hollow core floor and roof members

a = Plan location from building grid datum .... ± 1 in
a_1 = Plan location from centerline of steel* .... ± 1 in
b = Top elevation from nominal top elevation at member ends
    Covered with topping .... ± $3/4$ in
    Untopped floor .... ± $1/4$ in
    Untopped roof .... ± $3/4$ in
c = Maximum jog in alignment of matching edges
    (both topped and untopped construction) .... 1 in
d = Joint width
    0 to 40 ft member length .... ± $1/2$ in
    41 to 60 ft member length .... ± $3/4$ in
    61 ft plus .... ± 1 in
e = Differential top elevation as erected
    Covered with topping .... $3/4$ in
    Untopped floor .... $1/4$ in
    Untopped roof** .... $3/4$ in
f = Bearing length*** (span direction) .... ± $3/4$ in
g = Differential bottom elevation of exposed hollow-core slabs**** .... $1/4$ in

    * For precast concrete erected on a steel frame building, this tolerance takes precedence over tolerance on dimension "a".
    ** It may be necessary to feather the edges to ± $1/4$ in to properly apply some roof membranes.
    *** This is a setting tolerance and should not be confused with structural performance requirements set by the architect/engineer.
    **** Untopped installation will require a larger tolerance here.

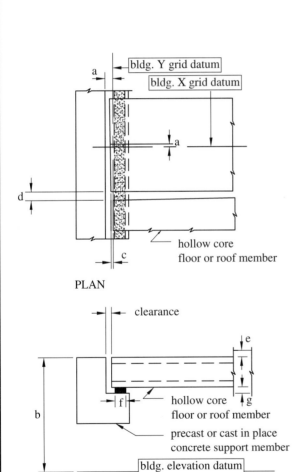

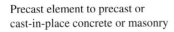

PLAN

ELEVATION

Precast element to precast or
cast-in-place concrete or masonry

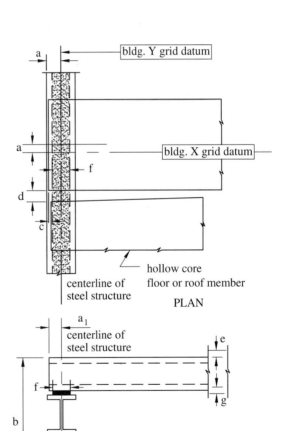

PLAN

ELEVATION

Precast element to structural steel

CHAPTER 2

DESIGN OF HOLLOW CORE SLABS

2.1 General

The design of hollow core slabs is governed by the ACI (318-95) Building Code Requirements for Structural Concrete.[2] As with prestressed concrete members in general, hollow core slabs are checked for prestress transfer stresses, handling stresses, service load stresses, deflections and design (ultimate) strength in shear and bending. For uniform load cases, the manufacturer's load tables will take into account these various design considerations and print a load capacity based on the governing criteria. For loading conditions other than uniform, or for the development of load tables, the design steps presented in this section are used.

An excellent reference for prestressed member design exists in the PCI Design Handbook.[1] Charts and tables provide design aids to shorten the calculation procedures. Another excellent source for design information is the PCI Standard Design Practice[4] which reflects design practices in the industry.

The generic slab presented in Section 1.7 will be used for the calculations presented in this section. The cross-section was selected to provide a means of demonstrating calculation procedures and does not represent any slab currently in use. Therefore, this generic slab should never be specified for use on a project. See Section 1.7 for the slabs currently available.

2.2 Flexural Design

2.2.1 ACI Requirements

Chapter 18 of ACI (318-95) presents provisions for the flexural design of prestressed concrete members. The applicable limits from ACI are paraphrased as follows:

2.2.1.1 Permissible stresses at transfer (Section 18.4).
  a) Extreme fiber stress in compression
     . . . . $0.6 f'_{ci}$

b) Extreme fiber stress in tension except as permitted in (c) . . . . $3 \sqrt{f'_{ci}}$
c) Extreme fiber stress in tension at ends of simply supported members . . . . . .
   . . . . $6 \sqrt{f'_{ci}}$

2.2.1.2 Permissible stresses at service loads (Section 18.4)
  a) Extreme fiber stress in compression due to prestress plus sustained loads
     . . . . $0.45 f'_c$
  b) Extreme fiber stress in compression due to prestress plus total load
     . . . . $0.60 f'_c$
  c) Extreme fiber stress in tension in precompressed tensile zone . . . . . $6 \sqrt{f'_c}$
  d) Extreme fiber stress in tension in precompressed tensile zone where deflections are calculated considering bilinear moment-deflection relationships
     . . . . $12 \sqrt{f'_c}$

2.2.1.3 Loss of prestress (Section 18.6)
  Calculation of losses shall consider:
  a) Seating loss
  b) Elastic shortening of concrete
  c) Creep of concrete
  d) Shrinkage of concrete
  e) Steel relaxation

2.2.1.4 Design (ultimate) strength
  a) Load Factors (Section 9.2)
     $U = 1.4D + 1.7L$
  b) Strength Reduction Factors (Section 9.3)
     Flexure $\phi = 0.9$
  c) Flexural Strength (Section 18.7)

$$M_u \leq \phi M_n = \phi A_{ps} f_{ps} \left(d_p - \frac{a}{2} \right)$$

$$a = \frac{A_{ps} f_{ps}}{0.85 f'_c b}$$

f_{ps} = value calculated by strain compatibility

or

$$f_{ps} = f_{pu}\left(1 - \frac{\gamma_p}{\beta_1}\rho_p\frac{f_{pu}}{f'_c}\right)$$

$$M_n > 1.2\,M_{cr}$$

2.2.2 Stresses at Transfer

When the prestressing strands are cut to apply the prestressing force to the concrete, only the slab self weight is present to counteract the effects of eccentric prestress. A check of stresses is required at this point to determine the concrete strength required to preclude cracking on the tension side or crushing on the compression side. The concrete strength at the time of transfer may be only 50% to 60% of the 28 day design strength.

Example 2.2.2.1 - Transfer Stresses

Using the generic hollow core cross-section defined in Section 1.7, check stresses at transfer of prestress using the following criteria:

Prestressing steel: 4 - $\frac{1}{2}''$ dia. 270 ksi, low relaxation strands.

$A_{ps} = 4(0.153) = 0.612$ in^2

assume 5% initial loss

$d_p = 7''$

$\ell = 30'\text{-}6''$

initial stress = 70% f_{pu}

Solution:

Stresses will be checked at the transfer point and at midspan

At release prestress force

$P_o = (0.70)(0.95)(0.612)(270) = 109.9$k

Prestress effect

$$= \frac{P_o}{A} \mp P_o\frac{e}{S}$$

$$= \frac{109.9}{154} \mp \frac{109.9(2.89)}{\begin{cases}297.9\\314.8\end{cases}}$$

$= -0.353$ ksi top fiber

$= +1.723$ ksi bottom fiber

Self weight at transfer point

$\ell t = 50d_b = 50(1/2) = 25$ in

moment 25 in from slab end

$$M_d = \left(\frac{30.5}{2}(2.08) - \frac{2.08^2}{2}\right)(0.0535)(3')$$

$= 4.74$ ft-k

$$\frac{M_d}{S} = \frac{(4.74)(12)}{\begin{cases}279.9\\314.8\end{cases}}$$

$= +0.191$ ksi top fiber

$= -0.181$ ksi bottom fiber

Net concrete stress at transfer point

$= -0.162$ ksi top fiber

$= +1.542$ ksi bottom fiber

Self weight at midspan

$$M_d = \frac{30.5^2}{8}(0.0535)(3') = 18.66 \text{ ft-k}$$

$$\frac{M_d}{S} = \frac{(18.66)(12)}{\begin{cases}279.9\\314.8\end{cases}}$$

$= +0.752$ ksi top fiber

$= -0.711$ ksi bottom fiber

Net concrete stress at midspan

$= +0.399$ ksi top fiber

$= +1.012$ ksi bottom fiber

Allowable stresses:

tension at end $= 6\sqrt{f'_{ci}}$

$$f'_{ci} = \left(\frac{-162}{6}\right)^2 = 729 \text{ psi}$$

tension at midspan $= 3\sqrt{f'_{ci}}$

does not control

compression $= 0.6\,f'_{ci}$

$$f'_{ci} = \frac{1542}{0.6} = 2570 \text{ psi}$$

Concrete strength required at release

$= 2570$ psi

Note that if tension or compression in the end region exceeds allowables based on a reasonable concrete release strength, strands may be debonded in some manufacturing systems or, for tension, top mild reinforcement may be used in some manufacturing systems to resist the total tension force.

If tension in the midspan region controls, either a high release strength must be used or mild reinforcement must be added to resist the total tension force. Mild reinforcement should only be used in the wet cast manufacturing system.

2.2.3 Prestress Losses

The calculation of prestress losses affects the service load behavior of a slab. The accuracy of any calculation method is dependent on the preciseness of concrete and prestressing steel material properties as well as external factors such as humidity used in the calculation procedure. The accuracy of loss calculations has little effect on the ultimate strength of a member.

Prestress loss calculations are required for prediction of camber and for service load stress calculations. Since the success of a project is judged on service load performance rather than ultimate strength, it behooves any slab producer to use a loss calculation procedure which best predicts the behavior of the product as produced.

For low relaxation strand and for special cases (e.g., long spans or special loadings) using stress relieved strand, the 1995 ACI Code references several sources for prestress loss calculations. The method presented here was developed by Zia, et al.[5] and considers the following parameters:

1) Elastic Shortening

$$ES = K_{es} \frac{E_s}{E_{ci}} f_{cir}$$

K_{es} = 1.0 for pretensioned members

$$f_{cir} = K_{cir} \left(\frac{P_i}{A} + \frac{P_i e^2}{I} \right) - \frac{M_g e}{I}$$

K_{cir} = 0.9 for pretensioned members

2) Concrete Creep

$$CR = K_{cr} \frac{E_s}{E_c} (f_{cir} - f_{cds})$$

K_{cr} = 2.0 for normal weight pretensioned members

= 1.6 for sand lightweight pretensioned members

$$f_{cds} = \frac{M_{sd} e}{I}$$

3) Shrinkage of Concrete

$$SH = 8.2 \times 10^{-6} K_{sh} E_s \left(1 - 0.06 \frac{V}{S} \right)$$
$$\times (100 - RH)$$

Fig. 2.2.3.1 Ambient relative humidity

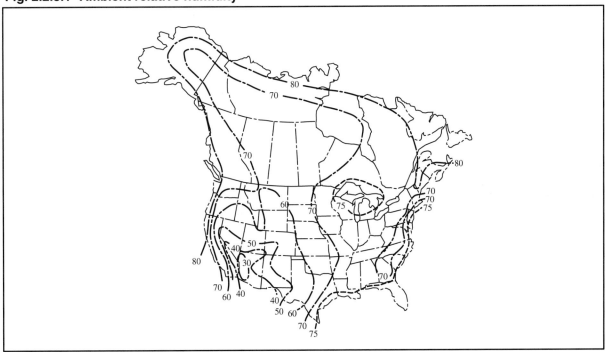

Table 2.2.3.1

Type of tendon	K_{re} psi	J
270 Grade stress-relieved strand or wire	20,000	0.15
250 Grade stress-relieved strand or wire	18,500	0.14
240 or 235 Grade stress-relieved wire	17,600	0.13
270 Grade low-relaxation strand	5000	0.040
250 Grade low-relaxation wire	4630	0.037
240 or 235 Grade low-relaxation wire	4400	0.035
145 or 160 Grade stress-relieved bar	6000	0.05

K_{sh} = 1.0 for pretensioned members

RH = Ambient relative humidity from Figure 2.2.3.1

4) Steel Relaxation

$$RE = [K_{re} - J(SH + CR + ES)]C$$

K_{re}, J, C = factors from Tables 2.2.3.1 and 2.2.3.2

5) Total Loss = ES + CR + SH + RE

Observations and experience in a plant may provide modifications to loss calculations to better predict slab performance.

Example 2.2.3.1 Loss of Prestress

Using the generic hollow core cross-section defined in Section 1.7, calculate the loss of prestress based on the following information:

Prestressing steel: 4-$\frac{1}{2}''$ dia. 270 ksi, low relaxation strands

$A_{ps}f_{pu} = 0.153(270) = 41.3$k/strand

$d_p = 7''$

initial stress = 70% f_{pu}

$\ell = 30'-6''$

Superimposed dead load = 20 psf

Table 2.2.3.2 Values of C

f_{si}/f_{pu}	Stress-relieved strand or wire	Stress-relieved bar or low-relaxation strand or wire
0.80		1.28
0.79		1.22
0.78		1.16
0.77		1.11
0.76		1.05
0.75	1.45	1.00
0.74	1.36	0.95
0.73	1.27	0.90
0.72	1.18	0.85
0.71	1.09	0.80
0.70	1.00	0.75
0.69	0.94	0.70
0.68	0.89	0.66
0.67	0.83	0.61
0.66	0.78	0.57
0.65	0.73	0.53
0.64	0.68	0.49
0.63	0.63	0.45
0.62	0.58	0.41
0.61	0.53	0.37
0.60	0.49	0.33

Solution:

1) Elastic Shortening

P_i = 0.7(4)(41.3k) = 115.6k

$$M_g = \frac{30.5^2}{8}(0.0535)(3')$$

= 18.66 ft-k

= 224 in-k

$$f_{cir} = 0.9\left(\frac{115.6}{154} + \frac{115.6(2.89)^2}{1224.5}\right)$$

$$- \frac{(224)(2.89)}{1224.5}$$

= 0.857 ksi

using E_s = 28,500 ksi and E_{ci} = 3250 ksi

$$ES = K_{es}\frac{E_s}{E_{ci}}f_{cir}$$

$$= (1.0)\frac{28500}{3250}(0.857)$$

= 7.52 ksi

2) Concrete Creep

$$f_{cds} = \frac{M_{sd}e}{I}$$

$$= \frac{\left(\frac{30.5^2}{8}\right)(0.02)(3)(12)(2.89)}{1224.5}$$

$$= 0.198 \text{ ksi}$$

using $E_c = 4300$ ksi and normal weight concrete

$$CR = K_{cr}\frac{E_s}{E_c}(f_{cir} - f_{cds})$$

$$= (2.0)\frac{28500}{4300}(0.857 - 0.198)$$

$$= 8.74 \text{ ksi}$$

3) Shrinkage of Concrete

$$\frac{V}{S} = \frac{Area}{Perimeter} = \frac{154}{2(36 + 8)} = 1.75$$

use RH = 70%

$$SH = 8.2 \times 10^{-6}K_{sh}E_s\left(1 - 0.06\frac{V}{S}\right)$$

$$\times (100 - RH)$$

$$= 8.2 \times 10^{-6}(1.0)28500$$

$$\times (1 - 0.06 \times 1.75)(100 - 70)$$

$$= 6.27 \text{ ksi}$$

4) Steel Relaxation

From Table 2.2.3.1

$K_{re} = 5000$, $J = 0.04$

From Table 2.2.3.2

$C = 0.75$ for $f_{si}/f_{pu} = 0.7$

$$RE = [K_{re} - J(SH + CR + ES)]C$$

$$= \left[\frac{5000}{1000} - 0.04x\right.$$

$$\left.(6.27 + 8.74 + 7.52)\right]0.75$$

$$= 3.07 \text{ ksi}$$

5) Total Loss at Midspan

$$= 7.52 + 8.74 + 6.27 + 3.07$$

$$= 25.6 \text{ ksi}$$

$$\% = \frac{25.6}{(0.7)(270)}(100) = 13.5\%$$

2.2.4 Service Load Stresses

Service load concrete stresses are calculated as a measure of performance or serviceability. For the in-service state when deflections must be calculated, a stress check must first be made to determine whether gross section properties or cracked-transformed section properties are to be used.

In-service stresses are checked assuming that all prestress losses have occurred. The calculated stresses are compared to the permissible stresses noted in Section 2.2.1. Hollow core slabs are normally designed to be uncracked under full service loads. Tensile stress limits of between $6\sqrt{f'_c}$ and $7.5\sqrt{f'_c}$ are commonly used. In special circumstances where deflections will not be a problem and where cracking will not be of concern, the upper limit of $12\sqrt{f'_c}$ can be used.

Example 2.2.4.1 Service Load Stresses

Using the generic hollow core cross-section defined in Section 1.7, calculate the service load stresses given the following criteria:

Prestressing steel:
4-$^1/_2''$ dia. 270 ksi, low relaxation strands

$A_{ps}f_{pu} = 0.153(270) = 41.3$ k/strand

$d_p = 7''$

Initial stress = 70% f_{pu}

$f'_c = 5000$ psi

$\ell = 30'-6''$

Clear Span = 30'-0"

Superimposed Dead Load = 20 psf
Live Load = 50 psf

Solution:

$$M_{sustained} = \frac{30^2}{8}(0.0535 + 0.020)$$

$$= 8.27 \text{ ft-k/ft} = 99.2 \text{ in-k/ft}$$

$$M_{service} = \frac{30^2}{8}(0.0535 + 0.020 + 0.050)$$

$$= 13.89 \text{ ft-k/ft} = 167 \text{ in-k/ft}$$

With losses = 13.5% from Example 2.2.3.1

$A_{ps}f_{se}$ = $(0.7)(4)(41.3)(1 - 0.135)$

= $100.0k$

Top fiber compression with sustained loads

$$f_{top} = \frac{100.0}{154} - \frac{100.0(2.89)}{297.9} + \frac{99.2(3)}{297.9}$$

= $0.649 - 0.970 + 0.999$

= $+0.679$ ksi

Permissible compression

= $0.45f'c$

= $0.45(5000)$

= 2.25 ksi > 0.679 ksi   OK

Top fiber compression with total load

$$f_{top} = \frac{100.0}{154} - \frac{100.0(2.89)}{297.9} + \frac{167(3)}{297.9}$$

= $0.649 - 0.970 + 1.679$

= 1.358 ksi

Permissible compression

= $0.60f'c$

= $0.60(5000)$

= 3.00 ksi > 1.358 ksi OK

Bottom fiber tension

$$f_{bottom} = 0.649 + (0.970 - 1.679)\frac{297.9}{314.8}$$

= -0.022 ksi (tension)

Permissible tension

= $7.5\sqrt{f'_c}$

= $7.5\sqrt{5000}$

= 0.530 ksi > 0.022 ksi OK

2.2.5 Design Flexural Strength

The moment capacity of a prestressed member is a function of the ultimate stress developed in the prestressing strands. As with non-prestressed concrete, upper and lower limits are placed on the amount of reinforcing to ensure that the stress in the strands is compatible with concrete stresses for ductile behavior.

The lower limit of reinforcing requires that:

$$\phi M_n \geq 1.2 M_{cr}$$

$$M_{cr} = \frac{I}{y_b}\left(\frac{P}{A} + \frac{Pe}{S_b} + 7.5\sqrt{f'_c}\right)$$

This ensures that when the concrete develops flexural cracks, the prestressing steel will not have reached its full design stress. Violation of this criteria might result in strand fractures at the point of flexural cracking with a resulting brittle failure. However, ACI (318-95) Section 18.8.3 allows violation of this requirement for flexural members with shear and flexural strength at least twice that required.

The upper limit of reinforcing requires that,

$$\omega_p \text{ or,}$$

$$\left[\omega_p + \frac{d}{d_p}(\omega - \omega')\right] \text{ or}$$

$$\left[\omega_{pw} + \frac{d}{d_p}(\omega_w - \omega'_w)\right]$$

be not greater than $0.36\beta_1$

The need for an upper limit on reinforcing is related to the assumptions of ultimate concrete compressive strain. Using a uniform compression stress block forces more concrete to reach ultimate strain as reinforcing ratios increase. Therefore when the upper reinforcing limit is exceeded, the moment capacity must be based on the compression block. For this condition,

$$\phi M_n = \phi\left[f'_c bd_p^2\left(0.36\beta_1 - 0.08\beta_1^2\right)\right]$$

for rectangular sections or for flanged sections with the neutral axis within the flange.

The stress in the prestressing steel at ultimate may be calculated in several ways. The ACI equation (18-3) may be used as an approximation, charts and tables from the PCI Design Handbook may be used, or a strain compatibility analysis may be made.

Example 2.2.5.1 Design Flexural Strength

Using the generic hollow core slab defined in Section 1.7, check the design flexural strength given the following criteria:

Prestressing steel: 4-$\frac{1}{2}$" dia., 270 ksi, low relaxation strands

$d_p = 7''$

initial stress = 70% f_{pu}

$f'c = 5000$ psi

$\ell = 30'-6''$

Clear span = $30'-0''$

Superimposed Dead Load = 20 psf

Live Load = 50 psf

Solution:

__METHOD 1:__ ACI Equation (18-3)

$$\phi M_n = \phi A_{ps} f_{ps} (d_p - a/2)$$

$$f_{ps} = f_{pu} \left[1 - \frac{\gamma_p}{\beta_1} \left(\rho_p \frac{f_{pu}}{f'_c} \right) \right]$$

Use $\gamma_p = 0.28$ for low relaxation strands

$$\beta_1 = 0.85 - \left(\frac{5000 - 4000}{1000} \right) 0.05$$

$$= 0.80$$

$$\rho_p = \frac{A_{ps}}{bd_p} = \frac{4(0.153)}{(36)(7)} = 0.0024$$

$$f_{ps} = 270 \left[1 - \frac{0.28}{0.80} \left(0.0024 \frac{270}{5} \right) \right]$$

$$= 257.7 \text{ ksi}$$

$$\omega_p = \frac{\rho_p f_{ps}}{f'_c} = \frac{0.0024(257.7)}{5}$$

$$= 0.124 < 0.36 \beta_1 = 0.288 \text{ OK}$$

$$a = \frac{A_{ps} f_{ps}}{0.85 f'_c b} = \frac{4(0.153)(257.7)}{(0.85)(5)(36)}$$

$$= 1.03 \text{ in}$$

Note: If "a" exceeds the top flange thickness, the compression block will encroach on the core area. For this situation, multiple compression forces are used for the internal couple as is done with other flanged members.

$$\phi M_n = 0.9(4)(0.153)(257.7) \left(7 - \frac{1.03}{2} \right)$$

$$= 920 \text{ in-k/slab} = 76.7 \text{ ft-k/slab}$$

$$w_u = 1.4(0.0535 + 0.02) + 1.7(0.05)$$

$$= 0.188 \text{ ksf}$$

$$M_u = \frac{30^2}{8} (0.188)$$

$$= 21.14 \text{ ft-k/ft}$$

$$= 63.4 \text{ ft-k/slab} < 76.7 \text{ OK}$$

Check minimum reinforcement

$$\phi M_n \geq 1.2 M_{cr}$$

From Example 2.2.3.1

$$\text{Loss} = 13.5\%$$

$$A_{ps} f_{se} = 0.7(4)(41.3)(1 - 0.135)$$

$$= 100.0 \text{ k}$$

Bottom compression

$$= \frac{100.0}{154} + \frac{100.0(2.89)}{314.8}$$

$$= 1.567 \text{ ksi}$$

$$M_{cr} = \frac{1224.5}{3.89} \left(1.567 + \frac{7.5 \sqrt{5000}}{1000} \right)$$

$$= 660 \text{ in-k/slab}$$

$$\frac{\phi M_n}{M_{cr}} = \frac{920}{660} = 1.39 > 1.2 \text{ OK}$$

__METHOD 2:__ PCI Design Handbook
Using Figure 4.12.2 from the 5th Edition Handbook.

$$\omega_{pu} = \frac{A_{ps} f_{pu}}{bd_p f'_c}$$

$$= \frac{4(41.3)}{(36)(7)(5)}$$

$$= 0.131$$

$$K'_u = 538$$

$$\phi M_n = K'_u \frac{bd_p^2}{12000}$$

$$= 538 \left(\frac{36(7)^2}{12000} \right)$$

$$= 79.0 \text{ ft-k/slab}$$

__METHOD 3:__ Strain Compatibility

The stress-strain diagram from Figure 11.2.5 of the PCI Design Handbook, shown in Fig. 2.2.5.1, will be used for this example. However, the actual stress-strain curves received with strand mill reports should be used when available.

The concrete ultimate strain is assumed to be 0.003 in/in. The method involves a trial and error procedure to obtain equilibrium within the section where the force in the compression block equals the tensile force in the steel. The equations are developed from the strain diagram shown.

$$a = \beta_1 c$$

Using 13.5% loss from Example 2.2.3.1

$$f_{se} = 0.7(270)(1 - 0.135) = 163.4 \text{ ksi}$$

Fig. 2.2.5.1 Stress-strain curves, prestressing strand

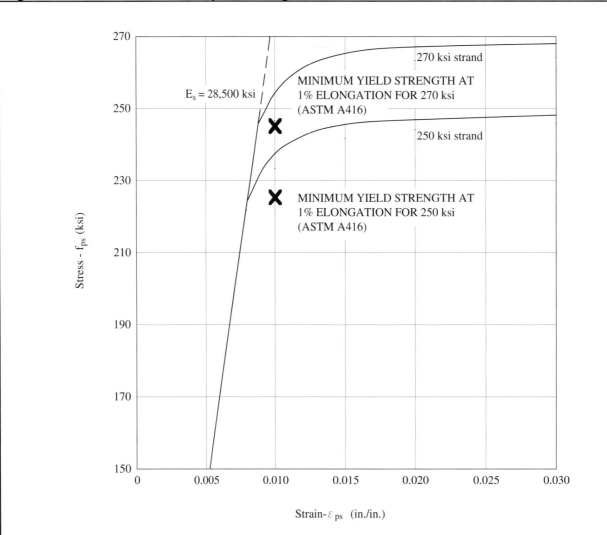

These curves can be approximated by the following equations:

250 ksi strand	270 ksi strand

$\varepsilon_{ps} \leq 0.0076$: $f_{ps} = 28{,}500\,\varepsilon_{ps}$ (ksi) || $\varepsilon_{ps} \leq 0.0086$: $f_{ps} = 28{,}500\,\varepsilon_{ps}$ (ksi)

$\varepsilon_{ps} > 0.0076$: $f_{ps} = 250 - \dfrac{0.04}{\varepsilon_{ps} - 0.0064}$ (ksi) || $\varepsilon_{ps} > 0.0086$: $f_{ps} = 270 - \dfrac{0.04}{\varepsilon_{ps} - 0.007}$ (ksi)

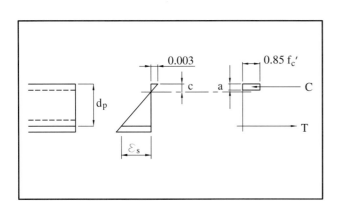

$$\varepsilon_{se} = \frac{f_{se}}{E_s} = \frac{163.4}{28500} = 0.0057$$

Assume c = 1″ then a = 0.80(1) = 0.8″

$$\varepsilon_s = \frac{d_p}{c}(0.003) - 0.003$$

$$= \frac{7}{1}(0.003) - 0.003 = 0.018$$

$$\varepsilon_{ps} = \varepsilon_{se} + \varepsilon_s$$

$$= 0.0057 + 0.018 = 0.0237$$

From stress-strain curve

$$f_{ps} = 268 \text{ ksi}$$

$$T = 4(0.153)(268) = 163.8$$

$$C = 0.85(5)(0.8)(36)$$

$$= 122.4k < 163.8k$$

Try c = 1.3″ then a = 0.80(1.3) = 1.04″

$$\varepsilon_s = \frac{7}{1.30}(0.003) - 0.003$$

$$= 0.0131$$

$$\varepsilon_{ps} = 0.0131 + 0.0057 = 0.0188$$

From stress-strain curve

$$f_{ps} = 267 \text{ ksi}$$

$$T = 4(0.153)(267) = 163$$

$$C = 0.85(5)(1.04)(36)$$

$$= 159k \approx 163k$$

$$\phi M_n = 0.9(4)(0.153)(267)\left(7 - \frac{1.04}{2}\right)$$

$$= 952 \text{ in-k/slab} = 79.3 \text{ ft-k/slab}$$

On occasion, conventional reinforcement is added to a hollow core slab to locally provide added flexural strength. When required, the bars are placed in cores right after the slab is cast and concrete is added to fill the cores with the bars. The following example illustrates the flexural strength calculation.

Example 2.2.5.2 Flexural Strength with Bars

Repeat Example 2.2.5.1 but add 2 - #4 bars in cores.

Solution:

Use strain compatibility for strength calculation with an effective depth of 5.5 in for the #4 bars.

Assume c = 1.53 in.

then a = 0.80(1.53) = 1.22 in

for strands

$$\varepsilon_s = \frac{7}{1.53}(0.003) - 0.003$$

$$= 0.0107 \text{ in/in}$$

$$\varepsilon_{ps} = 0.0057 + 0.0107$$

$$= 0.0164 \text{ in/in}$$

$$f_{ps} = 266 \text{ ksi}$$

for bars

$$\varepsilon_s = \frac{5.5}{1.53}(0.003) - 0.003$$

$$= 0.0078 \text{ in/in}$$

yield strain $= \dfrac{60}{29000} = 0.002 \text{ in/in}$

$$T = 4(0.153)(266) + 2(0.2)(60)$$

$$= 162.8 + 24$$

$$= 186.8k$$

$$C = 0.85(5)(1.22)(36)$$

$$= 186.7k \cong 186.8k \quad ok$$

$$\phi M_n = 0.9\left[162.8\left(7 - \frac{1.22}{2}\right) + 24\left(5.5 - \frac{1.22}{2}\right)\right]$$

$$= 1042 \text{ in-k}$$

$$= 86.8 \text{ ft-k}$$

2.3 Shear Design

2.3.1 ACI Requirements

Hollow core slabs are designed for shear according to the same ACI Code provisions used in general for prestressed members. In dry cast systems, the normal practice is to not provide stirrups when the applied shear exceeds shear capacity because of the difficulty encountered placing stirrups in most production processes. The placement of stirrups in a wet cast system is certainly easier than in a dry cast extruded system and is a viable shear enhancement method. An alternative used to increase shear capacity is to reduce the number of cores used in a given slab. This may be done by either leaving out a core for the entire length of a slab or by locally breaking into the cores and filling them solid while the concrete is still in a somewhat plastic state.

The provisions for shear are found in Chapter 11 of ACI 318-95. With some paraphrasing, the requirements are:

$$V_u \leq \phi V_n$$

$$\phi = 0.85 \text{ for shear}$$

$$V_n = V_c + V_s$$

For the purpose of this discussion, V_s, the contribution of shear reinforcement, will be taken as zero. The nominal concrete shear strength may be found using equation (11-9),

$$V_c = \left(0.6\sqrt{f'_c} + 700\frac{V_u d}{M_u}\right)b_w d \qquad (11\text{-}9)$$

when the effective prestress force is not less than 40 percent of the tensile strength of the flexural reinforcement. The term $V_u d/M_u$ shall not exceed 1.0. The minimum value for V_c may be used as $2\sqrt{f'_c}\,b_w d$ and the maximum value is the lesser of $5\sqrt{f'_c}\,b_w d$ or the value obtained from Equation (11-12) considering reduced effective prestress in the transfer zone.

Alternatively more refined shear calculations can be made according to the lesser of Equations (11-10) or (11-12).

$$V_{ci} = 0.6\sqrt{f'_c}\,b_w d + V_d + \frac{V_i M_{cr}}{M_{max}} \qquad (11\text{-}10)$$

$$V_{cw} = (3.5\sqrt{f'_c} + 0.3f_{pc})\,b_w d \qquad (11\text{-}12)$$

Equation (11-10) predicts shear strength for an inclined shear failure mode. For Equation (11-10), the following relationships are used:

$$M_{cr} = \left(\frac{I}{y}\right)(6\sqrt{f'_c} + f_{pe} - f_d) \qquad (11\text{-}11)$$

V_d = Unfactored self weight shear for non-composite sections

$V_i = V_u - V_d$

$M_{max} = M_u - M_d$

M_d = Unfactored self weight moment for non-composite sections

The minimum value for V_{ci} need not be less than $1.7\sqrt{f'_c}\,b_w d$ or $2\sqrt{f'_c}\,b_w d$ when the effective prestress force is not less than 40% of the tensile strength of the flexural reinforcement. For equations (11-10), (11-11) and (11-12), the reduction in prestressing force at the member end due to transfer must be considered. The ACI Code allows an assumption that prestressing force increases linearly from zero at the member end to full effective prestress in a length equal to 50 strand diameters.

Example 2.3.1.1 Shear Design

Using the generic hollow core cross-section defined in Section 1.7, check the slab for shear given the following information:

Prestressing steel: 4-$\frac{1}{2}$″ dia., 270 ksi, low relaxation strands.

Initial stress = 70% f_{pu} loss = 15%

f'_c = 5000 psi

ℓ = 25′-6″

Clear span = 25′-0″

Superimposed Dead Load = 20 psf
Live Load = 50 psf
Masonry dead load = 800 plf at 3′ from one support

Solution:

Uniform load: w_u = 1.4(0.0535 + 0.020) + 1.7(0.05)

= 0.188 ksf = 0.564 klf

Line Load: P_u = 1.4(0.800) = 1.12k/ft

= (3′)(1.12) = 3.36k

Load, shear and moment diagrams for 3′ slab width:

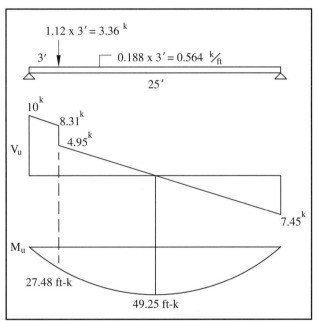

Using the more refined approach according to ACI Equations (11-10) or (11-12), ϕV_c is:

$$\phi V_{cw} = \frac{0.85}{1000}\left(3.5\sqrt{5000} + 0.3f_{pc}\right)$$
$$\times (10.5)(7) \qquad (11\text{-}12)$$

$$= 15.46 + 0.0187f_{pc}$$

f_{pc} is calculated as a function of the transfer of prestress into the section along the span.

transfer length = 50 d_b = 50(1/2) = 25″
with bearing length = 3″
full prestress transfer is achieved 22″ from the face of support

$A_{ps}f_{se} = 4(41,300)(0.70)(1 - 0.150)$

$$x \left(\frac{x+3}{25}\right) \text{ to } x = 22''$$

$$f_{pc} = \frac{A_{ps}f_{se}}{A} = \frac{98294}{154}\left(\frac{x+3}{25}\right)$$

$$\phi V_{cw} = 15.46 + 0.0187 \frac{98294}{154}\left(\frac{x+3}{25}\right)$$

$$= 15.46 + 11.96 \left(\frac{x+3}{25}\right) \text{ to } x = 22''$$

$$\phi V_{ci} = \left(0.6\frac{\sqrt{5000}}{1000}(10.5)(7) + V_d + \frac{V_iM_{cr}}{M_{max}}\right)$$

$$x\ 0.85 \qquad (11\text{-}10)$$

V_d = Shear due to unfactored self weight
     (for non-composite section)

$$= 3(0.0535)\left(\frac{25}{2} - x\right) = 2.01 - 0.16x$$

V_i = Shear due to factored loads minus V_d

$$M_{cr} = \left(\frac{I}{y_b}\right)\left(6\sqrt{f'_c} + f_{pe} - f_d\right)$$

$$f_{pe} = A_{ps}f_{se}\left(\frac{1}{A} + \frac{ey_b}{I}\right)$$

$$f_{pe} = 98.294\ x$$

$$\left[\frac{1}{154} + \frac{(3.89-1)(3.89)}{1224.5}\right]\left(\frac{x+3}{25}\right)$$

$$= 1.541\left(\frac{x+3}{25}\right) \leq 1.541 \text{ ksi}$$

f_d = flexural stress due to load used for V_d

$$= \frac{M_d}{S}$$

$$= \frac{\frac{(3)(0.0535)x}{2}(25-x)}{314.8}$$

$$= \frac{2.01x - 0.08x^2}{314.8}$$

$$M_{cr} = \frac{314.8}{12}\ x$$

$$\left[0.424 + f_{pe} - \frac{(2.01x - 0.08x^2)}{314.8}12\right]$$

$$= 11.130 + 26.233 f_{pe} - 2.01x + 0.8x^2$$

M_{max} = Moment due to factored
     loads minus M_d

Based on these definitions, ϕV_{cw}, ϕV_{ci}, and V_u are calculated at intervals across the span. A summary is presented in Table 2.3.1.1. Figure 2.3.1.1 presents the results graphically.

Table 2.3.1.1 Allowable Shear

x	V_u	ϕV_{cw}	ϕV_{ci}
h/2 = 0.333'	9.82^k	18.81^k	59.40^k
0.5'	9.72	19.76	45.74
1.0'	9.44	22.64	31.92
1.5'	9.16	25.51	27.15
2.0'	8.88	27.42	23.34
2.5'	8.59	27.42	18.93
3.0'	8.31	27.42	15.98
3.0'	4.95	27.42	10.02
3.5'	4.67	27.42	9.11
4.0'	4.39	27.42	8.34

Alternatively, the simplified equation (11-9) might be used.

$$\phi V_c = 0.85\left[0.6\sqrt{5000} + 700\left(\frac{V_u}{M_u}\right)(7)\right]$$

$$x\ \frac{10.5(7)}{1000}$$

$$= 2.65 + 306.1\frac{V_u}{M_u} \text{ (}M_u \text{ in in-k).}$$

The results of this equation are also shown on Figure 2.3.1.1.

At all points, $V_u < \phi V_c$ so shear strength is adequate and stirrups are not required.

2.4 Camber and Deflection

Camber is the upward deflection of a prestressed member and results from the prestressing force being eccentric from the center of gravity of the cross-section. Since both prestressing force and eccentricity are established by the required design load and span length, camber is a result of the design rather than a design parameter. Therefore, camber requirements should not be specified.

Deflections are also affected by the amount of prestressing only because prestressing establishes the load at which a member will crack. If tensile stresses are kept below cracking, deflections will be independent of the prestress level.

Cambers and deflections will change with time due to concrete creep, prestress loss and other fac-

Fig. 2.3.1.1 Shear for Example 2.3.1.1

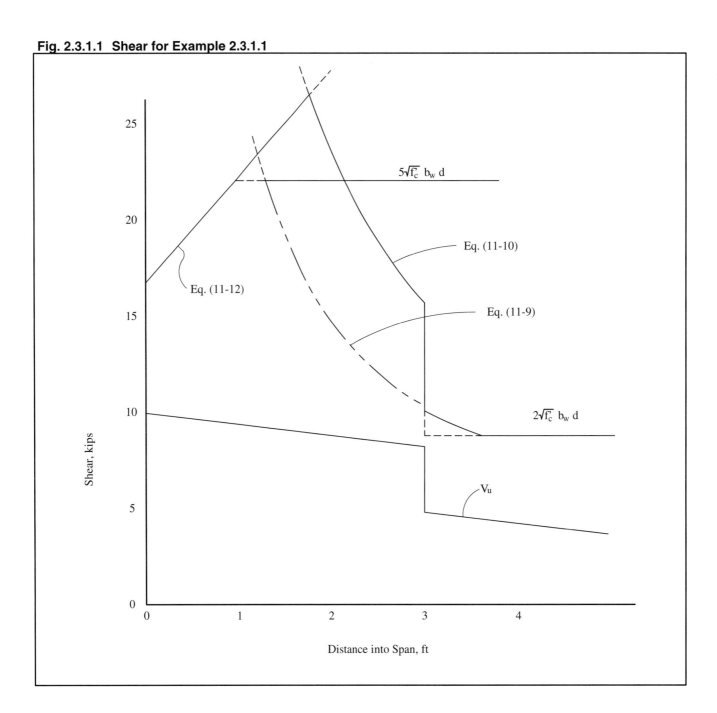

tors. The sustained compression due to the prestressing will cause camber growth. Balancing this is the effect of creep on deflections due to self weight and other sustained loads. It is this time dependent movement which, in addition to instantaneous deflections, must be considered in the development of framing schemes and detailing.

Instantaneous cambers and deflections are predictable as long as the material properties are known. The time dependent cambers and deflections are not predictable with any degree of accuracy and any calculation of long term movements must be considered to be only estimates.

This section presents calculation procedures for determining long term deflections. From the producer's standpoint, history and experience must be used to modify the procedures to fit the local product. From the specifier's standpoint, these procedures will allow only approximate estimates of long term effects and should be complemented with discussions with local producers.

2.4.1 Camber

Hollow core slabs are produced with straight strand patterns rather than using draped or depressed strands. Using (+) to indicate upward

Table 2.4.1 Long term multipliers[6]

Condition	Without Composite Topping	With Composite Topping
At Erection:		
1. Deflection (downward) component - apply to the elastic deflection due to the member weight at release of prestress	1.85	1.85
2. Camber (upward) component - apply to the elastic camber due to the prestress at the time of release of prestress	1.80	1.80
Final:		
3. Deflection (downward) component - apply to the elastic deflection due to the member weight at release of prestress	2.70	2.40
4. Camber (upward) component - apply to the elastic camber due to prestress at the time of release of prestress	2.45	2.20
5. Deflection (downward) - apply to elastic deflection due to superimposed dead load only	3.00	3.00
6. Deflection (downward) - apply to elastic deflection caused by the composite topping	—	2.30

movement and (–) to indicate downward movement, net camber can be calculated as:

$$\text{camber} = \frac{Pe\ell^2}{8EI} - \frac{5w\ell^4}{384EI}$$

To determine initial camber, the appropriate values for prestress force and modulus of elasticity of the concrete must be used. When ultimate moment rather than tensile stresses govern a design, the initial strand stress may be reduced to modify the anticipated camber. Additionally, slab camber is sensitive to support point locations during storage. Camber will increase as these support points move in from the slab ends.

Example 2.4.1 Initial Camber

Using the generic hollow core slab defined in section 1.7, calculate the initial camber given the following:

Prestressing steel: 4-$\frac{1}{2}$″ dia., 270 ksi, low relaxation strands

$A_{ps}f_{pu} = 0.153(270) = 41.3$k/strand

Initial stress: 70% f_{pu}

$$d_p = 7''$$
$$\ell = 30'\text{-}6''$$

Solution:

Estimate initial losses at 5% and use $E_{ci} = 3250$ ksi

$$P_o = 0.95(0.7)(4)(41.3) = 109.9^k$$

$$\text{camber} = \frac{109.9(3.89 - 1)[30.5(12)]^2}{(8)(3250)(1224.5)}$$

$$- \frac{5(3)(0.0535)(30.5)^4(1728)}{(384)(3250)(1224.5)}$$

$$= 1.34 - 0.79$$

$$= 0.55'' \text{ Say } \frac{1}{2}'' \text{ to } \frac{3}{4}'' \text{ initial camber}$$

Estimating long term effects is complicated because, as time passes, the prestressing force decreases due to losses and the modulus of elasticity of the concrete increases with concrete strength gain. Traditionally, a creep factor of 2.0 has been applied to instantaneous deflections to estimate the additional deflection due to creep. This has been modified by Martin[6] for prestressed concrete. Table 2.4.1 presents suggested multipliers to determine both long term final deflections and position at erection. It should be noted that in using these multipliers, a total deflection is calculated rather than the additional increment due to long term effects.

Example 2.4.2 Long Term Camber

For the slab of Example 2.4.1, determine the net camber at erection and the final camber.

Table 2.4.2 Maximum Permissible Computed Deflections[1]

Type of member	Deflection to be considered	Deflection limitation
Flat roofs not supporting or attached to non-structural elements likely to be damaged by large deflections	Immediate deflection due to live load L	$\dfrac{\ell}{180}$ *
Floors not supporting or attached to non-structural elements likely to be damaged by large deflections	Immediate deflection due to live load L	$\dfrac{\ell}{360}$
Roof or floor construction supporting or attached to nonstructural elements likely to be damaged by large deflections	That part of the total deflection occurring after attachment of nonstructural elements (sum of the long-term deflection due to all sustained loads and the immediate deflection due to any additional live load)**	$\dfrac{\ell}{480}$ ***
Roof or floor construction supporting or attached to nonstructural elements not likely to be damaged by large deflections		$\dfrac{\ell}{240}$ ****

* Limit not intended to safeguard against ponding. Ponding should be checked by suitable calculations of deflection, including added deflections due to ponded water, and considering long-term effects of all sustained loads, camber, construction tolerances, and reliability of provisions for drainage.

** Long-term deflection shall be determined in accordance with 9.5.2.5 or 9.5.4.2, but may be reduced by amount of deflection calculated to occur before attachment of nonstructural elements. This amount shall be determined on basis of accepted engineering data relating to time-deflection characteristics of members similar to those being considered.

*** Limit may be exceeded if adequate measures are taken to prevent damage to supported or attached elements.

**** But not greater than tolerance provided for nonstructural elements. Limit may be exceeded if camber is provided so that total deflection minus camber does not exceed limit.

Solution:

At erection,

initial camber = 1.34 − 0.79

= 0.55″ from Example 2.4.1

Erection camber = 1.34(1.80) − 0.79(1.85)

= 0.95″

Say 1″ erection camber

Final camber = 1.34(2.45) − 0.79(2.70)

= 1.15″

Say approximately 1 1/4″ final camber

2.4.2 Deflections

As with camber, concrete creep will also affect deflections due to sustained superimposed loads. These long term effects must be considered for comparison with Table 9.5(b) of the ACI Code to determine acceptability. This table is reproduced here as Table 2.4.2. Engineering judgement should be used in comparing calculated deflections to the ACI Code limits. Many building code specified live loads exceed the actual loads in a structure. While it may be implied that the full live load be used for comparison to Table 9.5(b), situations may arise where it is more reasonable to use actual anticipated live loads for deflection comparisons. A further complication for superimposed loads is that flexural cracking will reduce the effective moment of inertia of the section. Calculations using bilinear moment-deflection relationships are required when tension exceeds $6\sqrt{f'_c}$ and are covered extensively in references 1 and 2. By definition, cracking occurs at a tensile stress of $7.5\sqrt{f'_c}$. While the ACI Code requires such bilinear calculations when $6\sqrt{f'_c}$ tension is exceeded, in effect bilinear behavior is meaningless up to a tension of $7.5\sqrt{f'_c}$. Since hollow core slabs are normally designed to be uncracked under service loads, the effects of cracking will not be considered here.

Table 2.4.1 includes multipliers for determining the long term effects for superimposed loads. Again, use of the multipliers gives an estimate of total deflection rather than an increment for the additional long term deflection.

Example 2.4.3

For the slab of Examples 2.4.1 and 2.4.2, determine the total deflection due to a superimposed load of 20 psf dead and 50 psf live on a clear span of 30′-0″ including long term effects. Use $E_c = 4300$ ksi.

Solution:

From Example 2.4.2

Final camber = 1.15″

superimposed dead load instantaneous deflection:

$$= \frac{5(0.02)(3)(30)^4(1728)}{(384)(4300)(1224.5)} = 0.208″$$

Final deflection = 0.208 (3.0) = 0.62″

Instantaneous live load deflection:

$$= \frac{5(0.05)(3)(30)^4(1728)}{(384)(4300)(1224.5)} = 0.52''$$

Final position

final camber	=	+ 1.15″
sustained dead load	=	− 0.62
net camber		+ 0.53″
live load increment	=	− 0.52
		+ 0.01″

For comparison to the provisions of Chapter 9 of the ACI Code, when non-structural elements are attached to the slabs, the portion of deflection after erection may be used for comparison.

Change in camber	= 1.15″ − 0.95″ =	+ 0.20″
Sustained dead load	=	− 0.62″
Instantaneous live loads	=	− 0.52″
		− 0.94″

When a composite topping is used, it will be cast after a portion of the slab shrinkage has occurred. There will then be differential shrinkage between the topping and slab. This differential can cause additional deflection and bottom tensile stress. These effects will generally be negligible.

Example 2.4.4 Composite Slab

Given the slab of Example 2.4.3, add a 2″ composite topping and recalculate deflections including the affects of differential shrinkage.

Solution:

Final camber = 1.34 x 2.20 − 0.79 x 2.40

= 1.05″

Instantaneous topping weight deflection:

$$= \frac{5(0.025)(3)(30)^4(1728)}{(384)(4300)(1224.5)}$$

$$= 0.26''$$

Long term deflection due to topping weight

= 0.26″ (2.30) = 0.60″

Superimposed dead load deflection:

$$= \frac{5(0.02)(3)(30)^4(1728)}{(384)(4300)(2307)}$$

$$= 0.11''$$

(Note: 2307 in.^{4} = composite moment of inertia using a 3000 psi topping on a 5000 psi slab.)

Long term dead load deflection

= 0.11(3.0) = 0.33″

Instantaneous live load deflection:

$$= \frac{50}{20}(0.11) = 0.28''$$

Final Position = +1.05 − 0.60 − 0.33 − 0.26 = −0.14″ including instantaneous live load.

Calculate increment due to differential shrinkage assuming shrinkage strain of 500×10^{-6} in/in in both the topping and slab:

If total shrinkage	$= 500 \times 10^{-6}$
and erection shrinkage	$= 250 \times 10^{-6}$
differential shrinkage	$= 250 \times 10^{-6}$

The differential shrinkage can be thought of as a prestress force from the topping where

P = $A_{topping}$ (strain)(modulus)

= 36″(2″)(0.00025)(3320)

= 59.8k

The effect is lessened by concrete creep and, using a factor of 2.30 from Table 2.4.1, reduces to:

P = 59.8/2.30 = 26k

The eccentricity of this force is:

e = 9″ − 3.89″

= 5.11″

M = Pe = 26 x 5.11 = 133 in-k

downward deflection = $\frac{M\ell^2}{8EI}$

$$= \frac{133(30 \times 12)^2}{(8)(4300)(2307)}$$

$$= 0.22'' \cong 1/4''$$

Considering the span used in this example and the accuracy of the other camber and deflection calculations, it can be easily seen that differential shrinkage will generally not be significant.

2.5 Composite Design

A composite, structural concrete topping is commonly used in floor construction with hollow core slabs. The composite action is desirable to add stiffness and strength for gravity loads and may also be required for load transfer within a diaphragm. When a composite topping is used, consideration must be given to its strength, detailing and quality assurance.

The required compressive strength of the topping may be determined from the hollow core slab design requirements. Load tables provided by local producers will normally indicate that either a 3000 psi (20.7 MPa) or 4000 psi (27.6 MPa) concrete is required. Diaphragm requirements may necessitate a higher strength topping concrete.

From a detailing standpoint, the primary consideration is that hollow core slabs will have camber. If the topping is finished as a level surface, the camber will reduce the topping thickness in the midspan region which will affect the load capacity of the slabs. With significant topping thickness reduction, the integrity of the topping concrete may also be compromised. A preliminary slab design can provide an estimate of camber and the minimum topping thickness necessary to support the design loads. The first option is to provide the minimum thickness topping at midspan and allow the thickness to increase at the slab ends to maintain a flat floor. Finish and bearing elevations can then be set to this criteria.

A second option to minimize topping concrete volume is to allow the minimum topping thickness to follow the curvature of the slabs. This will result in a finished floor with camber which may be acceptable in some occupancies. In this option, it is important that all trades be made aware of the final camber as it may affect their work. Partitions, doorways and stairs will be particularly affected in this option.

When control joints are used in a structural topping, they should be located over the joints in the precast units below where cracks would most naturally occur in the topping. At the ends of slabs, where movement will occur due to camber changes, deflections, creep, shrinkage or elastic shortening, control joints are desirable.

Reinforcing of a topping may be required for structural design. If not, consideration should be given to using minimum shrinkage reinforcement for crack control.

Since the composite topping and hollow core slabs interact to create the final structural element, it is imperative that the topping bond well with the slabs. While the building designer may only be interested in the final product, the process of achieving a well bonded, composite topping is very important. The hollow core producer is dependent on a properly bonded topping, yet is not involved in specifying, designing or installing the topping. The hollow core producer is responsible for supplying a slab that is capable of bonding with a topping. The installer of the topping is responsible for surface preparation, topping concrete mix design and curing to assure proper bond.

At a minimum, the slab surface must be clean and damp at the time of topping installation. It is recommended that the surface be thoroughly saturated prior to topping placement, but all standing water must be removed. ACI 301-96[7] specifies that a sand and cement grout be scrubbed into the slab surface ahead of topping placement. If this procedure is used, it is imperative that initial set not be allowed prior to topping placement. If initial set occurs, the grout can become a bond breaker. Similarly, bonding agents, which are rarely specified, will also act as a bond breaker if any initial set occurs prior to topping placement.

The topping concrete mix and curing techniques will also affect bond of a composite topping. Curling at topping edges or joints will cause local delamination. Curling is a result of differential shrinkage between the top and bottom surfaces of the topping. Generally, water is lost more quickly from the top surface causing additional drying shrinkage. This can be minimized by proper curing techniques and low shrinkage concrete.

Design of hollow core slabs for composite action is usually limited to a horizontal shear strength of 80 psi (0.5 MPa) according to section 17.5.2.1 of ACI 318-95. Through limited published[8] and unpublished testing, the machine finished surface has been found to meet the requirements of that section. The horizontal shear check should be based on the shear diagram rather than using an average horizontal shear over the distance from zero moment to maximum moment when checking compliance with the 80 psi limit.

Composite ties are not normally provided given the difficulty and expense of installing the ties in a machine casting operation. When the horizontal shear exceeds 80 psi (0.5 MPa) and composite ties are not used, the topping is considered to be superimposed dead load on a non-composite slab. In a wet cast system, horizontal shear ties with $^1/_4$ in amplitude roughening may be used to take advantage of the higher stresses allowed by ACI.

Design of a composite section is similar to that presented in Sections 2.2 and 2.3. The following example demonstrates the additional considerations with a composite section.

Example 2.5.1 Composite Design

Using the generic hollow core cross-section defined in Section 1.7, add a 2 in structural topping and check for the following conditions:

Prestressing steel: 4-$\frac{1}{2}''$ dia., 270 ksi low relaxation strands

Initial stress: 70% f_{pu}

d_p: 7 in

Slab: f'_c = 5000 psi

$\quad\quad\quad E_{ci}$ = 3250 ksi

$\quad\quad\quad E_c$ = 4300 ksi

Topping: f'_c = 3000 psi

$\quad\quad\quad E_c$ = 3320 ksi

Slab length: 30'-6"

Slab span: 30'-0"

Loads: topping = 25 psf
$\quad\quad\quad$ dead load = 20 psf
$\quad\quad\quad$ live load = 50 psf

Calculate section properties:

Base section   A = 154 in^2
$\quad\quad\quad\quad\quad$ I = 1224.5 in^4
$\quad\quad\quad\quad\quad$ y_b = 3.89 in

Topping

$\quad$ n = 3320/4300 = 0.77

$\quad$ use width = 0.77(36)
$\quad\quad\quad\quad\quad$ = 27.7 in

Composite

$\quad$ A = 154 + 2(27.7) = 209.4 in^2

$\quad y_b = \dfrac{154(3.89) + 2(27.7)(9)}{209.4}$

$\quad\quad$ = 5.24 in.

I = $1224.5 + 154(5.24 - 3.89)^2$

$\quad\quad + \dfrac{2^3}{12}(27.7) + 2(27.7)(9 - 5.24)^2$

$\quad$ = 2307 in^4

Calculate prestress losses:

From Example 2.2.3.1

ES = 7.52 ksi

Concrete creep

$M_{sd} = \dfrac{30^2}{8}(0.025 + 0.020)(3)$

$\quad\quad$ = 15.19 ft-k

$f_{cds} = \dfrac{15.19(12)(2.89)}{1224.5}$

$\quad\quad$ = 0.430 ksi

$CR = (2.0)\dfrac{28500}{4300}(0.857 - 0.430)$

$\quad\quad$ = 5.66 ksi

SH = 6.27 ksi

$RE = \left[\dfrac{5000}{1000} - 0.04(6.27 + 5.66 + 7.52)\right]0.75$

$\quad\quad$ = 3.17 ksi

Loss = 7.52 + 5.66 + 6.27 + 3.17

$\quad\quad$ = 22.62 ksi = 12%

Calculate service load stresses:

$A_{ps}f_{se} = 0.7(4)(41.3)(1 - 0.12)$

$\quad\quad$ = 101.8k

$M_{non-comp} = \dfrac{30^2}{8}(0.0535 + 0.025)$

$\quad\quad$ = 8.83 ft-k/ft = 106 in-k/ft

$M_{comp} = \dfrac{30^2}{8}(0.020 + 0.050)$

$\quad\quad$ = 7.88 ft-k/ft = 94.5 in-k/ft

At top of topping

$f_{top} = \dfrac{94.5(3)(10 - 5.24)}{2307}(0.77)$

$\quad\quad$ = 0.450 ksi

At top of slab

$f_{top} = \dfrac{101.8}{154} - \dfrac{101.8(2.89)(4.11)}{1224.5}$

$\quad\quad + \dfrac{106(3)(4.11)}{1224.5} + \dfrac{94.5(3)(8 - 5.24)}{2307}$

$\quad\quad$ = 1.080 ksi

At bottom of slab

$f_{bottom} = \dfrac{101.8}{154} + \dfrac{101.8(2.89)(3.89)}{1224.5}$

$\quad\quad - \dfrac{106(3)(3.89)}{1224.5} - \dfrac{94.5(3)(5.24)}{2307}$

$\quad\quad$ = –0.058 ksi

Calculate flexural strength

$w_u = 1.4(0.0535 + 0.025 + 0.020)$
$\quad\quad + 1.7(0.050)$

$\quad\ = 0.223$ ksf

$M_u = \dfrac{30^2}{8}(0.223)(3)$

$\quad\ = 75.26$ ft-k

Using ACI Eq. (18-3)

$\rho_p = \dfrac{4(0.153)}{36(9)} = 0.0019$

$f_{ps} = 270\left[1 - \dfrac{0.28}{0.85}\left(0.0019\dfrac{270}{3}\right)\right]$

$\quad\ = 254.8$ ksi

$a = \dfrac{4(0.153)(254.8)}{0.85(3)(36)}$

$\quad = 1.7$ in

$\phi M_n = 0.9(4)(0.153)(254.8)\left(9 - \dfrac{1.7}{2}\right)$

$\quad\quad = 1144$ in-k $= 95.3$ ft-k

Check $1.2\ M_{cr}$

$f_{bottom} = \dfrac{101.8}{154} + \dfrac{101.8(2.89)(3.89)}{1224.5}$

$\quad\quad\ = 1.596$ ksi

$M_{cr} = \dfrac{2307}{5.24}\left(1.596 + \dfrac{7.5\sqrt{5000}}{1000}\right)$

$\quad\ = 936$ in-k

$\dfrac{\phi M_n}{M_{cr}} = \dfrac{1144}{936} = 1.22 > 1.2$ ok

Check horizontal shear:

$\phi V_{nh} = \phi 80 b_v d$

$\quad\quad = 0.85(80)(36)(9)$

$\quad\quad = 22030$ lb

$\quad\quad = 22$ k

at h/2

$V_u = \left(\dfrac{30}{2} - \dfrac{10}{2(12)}\right)(0.223)(3)$

$\quad = 9.8$ k < 22 k ok

Section is composite

Check web shear at h/2:

transfer length $= 50(0.5) = 25$ in

at h/2 plus 3 in bearing

$A_{ps}f_{se} = 101.8\left(\dfrac{8}{25}\right) = 32.6$ k

for composite section, f_{pc} is calculated at centroid of composite section

$f_{pc} = \dfrac{32.6}{154} - \dfrac{32.6(2.89)(5.24 - 3.89)}{1224.5}$

$\quad\ = 0.108$ ksi

$\phi V_{cw} = 0.85\left[\dfrac{3.5\sqrt{5000}}{1000} + 0.3(0.108)\right](10.5)(9)$

$\quad\quad = 22.5$k > 9.8 k ok

Check inclined shear at 4 ft

$V_u = \left(\dfrac{30}{2} - 4\right)(0.223)(3)$

$\quad = 7.36$k

$V_d = \left(\dfrac{30}{2} - 4\right)(0.0535 + 0.025 + 0.020)(3)$

$\quad = 3.25$k

$V_i = 7.36 - 3.25 = 4.11$k

$M_u = 0.223(3)(4)\left(\dfrac{30}{2} - \dfrac{4}{2}\right) = 34.8$ ft-k

$M_d = (0.0535 + 0.025 + 0.020)(3)(4)\left(\dfrac{30}{2} - \dfrac{4}{2}\right)$

$\quad\ = 12.25 + 3.12 = 15.37$ ft-k

$M_{max} = 34.8 - 15.37 = 19.43$ ft-k

$f_{pe} = \dfrac{101.8}{154} + \dfrac{101.8(2.89)(3.89)}{1224.5}$

$\quad\ = 1.596$ ksi

$f_d = \dfrac{12.25(12)(3.89)}{1224.5} + \dfrac{3.12(12)(5.24)}{2307}$

$\quad = 0.552$ ksi

$M_{cr} = \dfrac{2307}{5.24}\left(\dfrac{6\sqrt{5000}}{1000} + 1.596 - 0.552\right)$

$\quad\ = 646$ in-k $= 53.9$ ft-k

$\phi V_{ci} = 0.85\left[\dfrac{0.6\sqrt{5000}}{1000}(10.5)(9)\right]$

$\quad\quad + 0.85\left[3.25 + \dfrac{4.11(53.9)}{19.43}\right]$

$\quad\quad = 15.86$k > 7.36k ok

Fig. 2.6.1.1

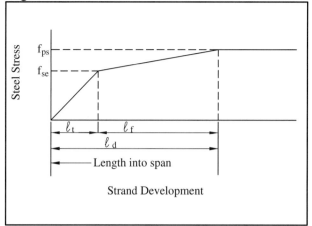

Strand Development

Fig. 2.6.1.2

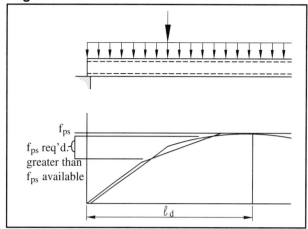

2.6 Strand Development

2.6.1 ACI Requirements

Section 12.9 of the ACI Code covers development length for prestressing strands. While the topic has received considerable discussion[9-16], the ACI Code expression currently remains:

$$\ell_d = (f_{ps} - 2/3f_{se})d_b$$

A further requirement is that the development length shall be doubled when bonding of a strand does not extend to the end of the member and the precompressed tensile zone is allowed to be in tension at service loads.

The ACI Code expression for development length describes two bond mechanisms. The first is the transfer length which is the bond length required to transfer the effective prestress after losses, f_{se}, to the concrete. This portion of the development length is:

$$\ell_t = \frac{f_{se}}{3}d_b$$

With f_{se} equal to 150 ksi (1034 MPa), the transfer length becomes $50d_b$, the length used for shear calculations.

The second mechanism is for bond length after the steel stress increases above f_{se}. To develop the full design strength of the strand, f_{ps}, a bond length in addition to the transfer length is required. The flexural bond length is expressed as:

$$\ell_f = (f_{ps} - f_{se})d_b$$

Figure 2.6.1.1 depicts the increase in steel stress along the development length of the strand.

Section 12.9.2 of the ACI Code limits investigation of development length to the section nearest the end of the member where full design strength is required. In conventionally reinforced concrete, the rate of moment increase must be considered in selecting reinforcing bar sizes. This consideration is also valid in prestressed concrete members. As shown in Figure 2.6.1.2, with a steep rate of moment increase, critical sections may occur in the strand development length at less than maximum moment.

Demand on strand strength above f_{se} does not occur until after flexural cracking occurs. If flexural cracking occurs in the transfer length, the strand cannot accept additional stress so bond failure occurs. Therefore, the limit on member flexural strength in the strand transfer length is the cracking moment.

In the flexural bond length, strand stress can increase above f_{se}, but not to full f_{ps}. Therefore, there is additional flexural strength above the cracking moment, but less than full nominal strength. If flexural cracking occurs at factored load in the flexural bond length, the maximum value for f_{ps} can be calculated as:

$$f'_{ps} = f_{se} + \frac{(x - \ell_t)}{\ell_f}(f_{ps} - f_{se})$$

where x = the distance from the end of the member to the section of interest

The nominal moment capacity is then calculated on the basis of this maximum strand stress.

Martin and Korkosz[17] suggest that with partially developed strand, the full concrete compressive failure strain will not be achieved. A strain compatibility analysis can be performed to determine the concrete strain that would be consistent with f'_{ps} and nominal strength can then be calculated using that strain.

When debonded strands are mixed with fully bonded strands, a similar strain compatibility analysis may be required in the flexural bond length for the debonded strands. In this case, nominal strength can be calculated in two ways:

1. Analyze section with all strands at the f'_{ps} for the debonded strands.

2. Analyze section with only fully bonded strands at their f_{ps} and ignore the debonded strands.

The greater of the two results would predict the nominal strength of the section.

For hollow core slabs, the strain compatibility analysis for partially developed strand will yield variable results as compared to a traditional approach where f'_{ps} is used with a full concrete strain of 0.003 in/in. If f'_{ps} is close to f_{se}, the strain compatibility analysis will predict moment capacity of about 85% of the traditional analysis. When f'_{ps} is 10% greater than f_{se}, the difference reduces to 5% or less. The additional complexity of the strain compatibility analysis would only seem warranted when flexural cracking is expected near the transfer point or when debonded strands are used.

There are several aspects of a bond length discussion that are significant to hollow core slab design. In many framing schemes, there will be a requirement to use very short slabs to fill in an area. With fully developed strands, these slabs will normally have very large load capacities. However, capacity may be reduced because the strands might only be partially developed. For example, for a slab prestressed with $1/2''$ (12.7 mm) ϕ, 270 ksi (1860 MPa) strands with f_{se} = 150 ksi (1034 MPa) and f_{ps} = 260 ksi (1790 MPa):

$$\ell_d = \left(f_{ps} - \frac{2}{3}f_{se}\right)d_b$$

$$= \left[260 - \frac{2}{3}(150)\right](0.5)$$

$$= 80'' = 6'\text{-}8'' \text{ (2030 mm)}$$

This slab would have to be two development lengths, or 13'-4" (4.1 m) long in order to develop its full design strength. A shorter slab would have reduced capacity.

Hollow core slab systems are often required to carry concentrated or wall loads which may affect the rate of moment increase near the member end. While not required by ACI, it is suggested that the transfer length and flexural bond length regions be investigated for reduced capacity when the moment gradient is high.

The development length equations in the ACI Code are based on testing conducted with members cast with concrete having normal water-cement ratios. As noted in the Commentary to the ACI Code, no slump concrete requires extra precautions. Hollow core slabs produced with the extrusion process fall into this category. As originally presented by Anderson and Anderson[10] and reinforced by Brooks, Gerstle and Logan[18], a measure of satisfactory bond is the free end slip of a member after it is cut to length. A limit on free end slip expressed as:

$$\delta_{all} = \frac{f_{se}f_{si}}{6E_s}d_b$$

has been suggested as a maximum free end strand slip for using the ACI Code development lengths. This expression approximates the strand shortening that would have to occur over the transfer length. For a $1/2''$ (12.7 mm) dia. strand stressed initially to 189 ksi (1300 MPa), the free end slip should not exceed about $3/32''$ (2.4 mm) if the ACI Code transfer and development lengths are to be used.

When free end slip exceeds δ_{all}, the transfer length and the flexural bond length will increase. Shear strength in the transfer length and moment capacity in the flexural bond length will be decreased and the length into the span where full moment capacity is provided will be increased.

If the free end strand slip is known from quality control measurements, the member capacity can be evaluated with consideration of extended transfer and flexural bond lengths. As a function of measured end slip, the transfer length and flexural bond length can be calculated for each strand as follows:

$$\ell_t = 2\delta_s E_s/f_{si}$$

$$\ell_f = 6\delta_s E_s(f_{ps} - f_{se})/(f_{si}f_{se})$$

Shear strength can be evaluated by substituting the extended transfer length for 50 d_b in evaluating the rate of increase of prestress. Flexural

Fig. 2.6.1.3 Effect of End Slip

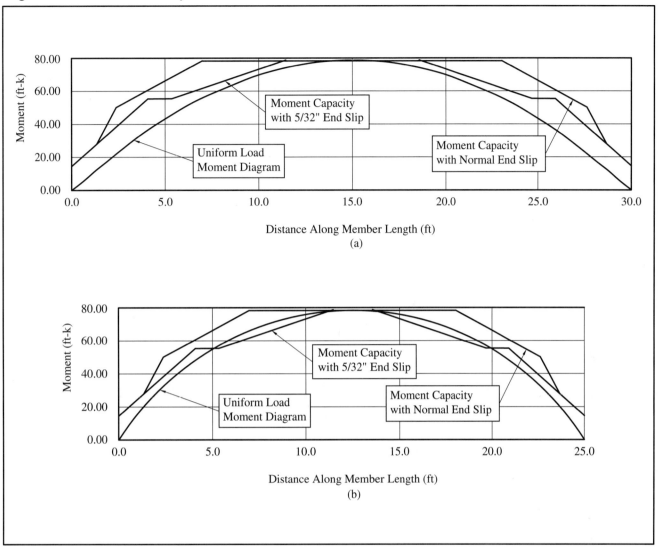

strength calculations are affected only by the extension of the strand development length and potential reduction of f'_{ps}. The strain compatibility analysis suggested by Martin and Korkosz for sections with partially developed strand becomes more complex as there can be variation in development lengths within a given member.

Figure 2.6.1.3 illustrates the change in moment capacity for the generic slab of Section 1.7 from normal slip to $^5/_{32}$ in (4 mm) slip on all strands. In (a), the span length is 30 ft (9.1 m) and there would be no change in slab capacity for uniform load. In (b), the span is reduced to 25 ft (7.6 m) and it is clear that the extended development length would result in reduced capacity even with uniform load. End slip in excess of normal slip has a more significant effect in shorter slabs.

The following example demonstrates the use of the Martin and Korkosz strain compatibility analysis for partially developed strand and the use of free end slip for evaluating strength. The procedure illustrated is also valid with normal end slip by using the appropriate transfer and bond lengths.

Example 2.6.1.1 Initial Strand Slip

Given the generic hollow core slab defined in Section 1.7, calculate the design flexural strength given the following:

Prestressing steel: 4-$^1/_2''$ dia., 270 ksi low
relaxation strands.

E_s = 28500 ksi

d_p = 7″

f'_c = 5000 psi

f_{si} = 185 ksi

f_{se} = 163.4 ksi

f_{ps} = 267 ksi

δ_s = $^3/_{16}$ in. all strands

Solution:

ℓ_t = 2($^3/_{16}$)(28500)/185

   = 57.8″

ℓ_f = 6($^3/_{16}$)(28500)(267 − 163.4)/185/163.4

   = 109.9″

ℓ_d = 57.8 + 109.9

   = 167.7″

The minimum slab length required to achieve full flexural capacity is 2(167.7)/12 or 28 ft. Calculate flexural capacity at 10 ft.

f'_{ps} = 163.4 + $\dfrac{(10\text{x}12 − 57.8)}{109.9}$ (267 − 163.4)

   = 222 ksi

$A_{ps}f'_{ps}$ = 4(0.153)(222)

   = 135.9k

Traditional analysis

a = $\dfrac{135.9}{.85(5)(36)}$ = 0.89 in.

M_n = 135.9(7 − 0.89/2)/12

   = 74.24 ft-k

Strain compatibility analysis

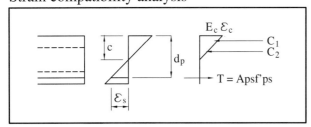

ε_{ps} = $\varepsilon_{se} + \varepsilon_s$

ε_{se} = 163.4/28500

   = 0.00573 in/in

ε_{ps} = 222/28500

   = 0.00779 in/in

ε_s = 0.00779 − 0.00573

   = 0.00206 in/in

Using trial and error for

T = C

Find

c = 2.18″

ε_c = 0.000929 in/in

Concrete stress at top

   = 4300(0.000929)

   = 3.995 ksi

Concrete stress at top of core

   = $\dfrac{(2.18 − 1.25)}{2.18}$ (3.995) = 1.704 ksi

C_1 = $\dfrac{(3.984 + 1.704)}{2}$ (1.25)(36)

   = 128k

C_2 = $\dfrac{1.704}{2}$ (10.5)(2.18 − 1.25)

   = 8.3k

M_n = (135.9(7 − 0.54) − 8.3(1.56 − 0.54))/12

   = 72.45 ft-k

CHAPTER 3

SPECIAL DESIGN CONSIDERATIONS

3.1 General Information

The application of hollow core slabs as roof and floor deck members creates several situations for consideration in design which are either not completely covered by ACI Code provisions or which involve consideration of production processes. This section presents information which may be used as a guideline for the situations described but not as hard and fast rules. The criteria presented represent conservative practices and should be verified with local producers. Published data relative to each situation is referenced. However, extensive in plant testing has been conducted by hollow core producers which may allow less conservative criteria to be used because of the unique characteristics of a particular slab.

3.2 Load Distribution

As demonstrated in Chapter 2 of this manual, hollow core slabs are designed as individual, one way, simple span slabs. When the slabs are installed and grouted together at the keyways, the individual slabs become a system that behaves similarly to a monolithic slab. A major benefit of the slabs acting together is the ability to transfer forces from one slab to another. In most hollow core slab deck applications, non-uniform loading occurs in the form of line loads, concentrated loads, or load concentrations at openings. The ability of individual slabs to interact allows these load concentrations to be shared by several slabs. The ability to distribute loads among several slabs has been demonstrated in several published tests [19-25] and many unpublished tests.

In many cases, load concentrations do not have to be carried by the slabs. For example, a header at a large opening may be supported directly to a foundation or vertical support element; a beam might be installed to directly carry a heavy concentrated load; or a heavy wall parallel to a slab span might be designed to carry its own weight or any load superimposed on the wall as a deep beam spanning between vertical supports. However, when such loads must be supported by the slab system, a method is required to decide how many slabs will contribute in carrying a given load in a given location. This section presents a design method that may be used when the slabs do actually have to support non-uniform loads.

3.2.1 Load Distribution Mechanisms

As load is applied to one slab in a system, the response of the slab system is to deflect and also twist if the load is not on the longitudinal centerline of the system. As the loaded slab edges try to move down, the interlock of the grout in the joints with the keyways formed in the slab edges forces adjacent slabs to deflect a similar amount. The flexural and torsional stiffness of the adjacent slabs reduce the deflection of the loaded slab from what might be expected if the slab were alone. Shear forces are developed along the keyways and the loaded slab then gets some support from the adjacent slabs. As this effect trickles through the system, the keyways between slabs force equal deflections for slab edges at any given keyway.

Many times shrinkage cracks will occur in the grouted joints at the interface between the grout and slab edge. This cracking does not impair the mechanism described above because the configuration of the keyways in the slab edges still provides mechanical interlock even with the presence of a crack.

Shear forces transferred along keyways cause two sets of forces that are normally not considered in hollow core slab design. The first is torsion which develops because the shear on one edge of a given slab is different in magnitude from the shear on the opposite edge. As depicted in Figure 3.2.1, the keyway shears reduce as the distance from the load increases. These torsions cause shear stress in the slabs in addition to the direct shear stress.

The second set of forces is induced because the system is tending to behave as a two way slab. Transverse bending moments occur because of the edge support provided by adjacent slabs. The result is transverse tensile stress developed in the bottom of the slab and compressive stress in the top. Hollow core slabs are not provided with transverse reinforcement. Transverse tensile

Fig. 3.2.1

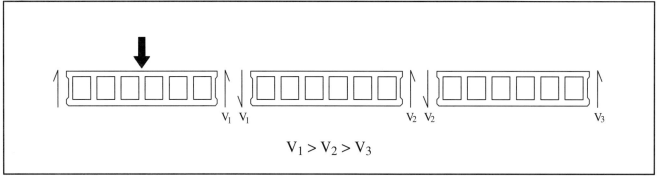

$$V_1 > V_2 > V_3$$

stresses must then be resisted by plain concrete. The magnitude of load concentration causing the transverse tension must be limited to preclude a splitting failure. See Section 3.2.2.

Several factors affect the ability of a slab system to distribute loads to adjacent slabs. As the width of an assembly of slabs gets narrower than the span length, a reduction in the number of slabs contributing to the support of a concentration of load occurs. This occurs because the freedom of the free edges of the system to deflect and twist becomes more significant. A second factor is the spacing of the slab joints. With slabs available in widths ranging from 2 feet to 8 feet (0.6 to 2.4 m), some differences in load distribution behavior can be expected. Finally, the span length affects the number of contributing slabs. As span length changes for a wide system, the interaction of flexural and torsional stiffnesses changes. For longer spans, flexural stiffness reduces relative to torsional stiffness. This results in relatively less slab rotation and less transverse curvature. The result is that more slabs can contribute to distribution on longer spans as long as the system is wide relative to its length.

3.2.2 Design Guidelines

ACI 318-95 recognizes the load transfer capabilities of hollow core slabs in Section 16.3.1. That section specifies that distribution of forces be established by analysis or test. The guidelines presented here were based on extensive, full scale testing of a specific slab system. Additionally, a comparison of these guidelines to an analytical study has been done. Therefore, the guidelines presented here should satisfy the requirement of ACI (318-95) 16.3.1.

The two basic design parameters considered for hollow core slabs are flexure and shear. Design for flexure is straightforward with the effective load resisting width being a function of the span length. Conversely, shear design is complicated by torsions developed in the system. If torsion is not to be used as a design parameter, direct shear must then be modified to reflect the increase in shear stress from the torsion.

Figure 3.2.2 depicts a method of establishing an effective resisting section for any type of load to be distributed between slabs. In the midspan regions, the effective width is defined as a function of span length. At the supports, the effective width is defined as an absolute width. The width at the support is restricted to account for shear stresses due to torsion. Use of these resisting sections will result in prediction of peak values of moment and shear. That is, the effective width concept is simply a mechanism used to determine the maximum design moments and shears rather than a depiction of the actual load path through the system.

The performance of slab systems indicates that shear and moment might affect additional slabs. For example, for a load located some distance from a free edge, the peak moment due to that load can be predicted by assuming the load is resisted by a width equal to 0.50ℓ. In reality, in flexure, a total width equal to 85% to 90% of the span length might have some moment attributable to that load. In shear, the 1'-0" (0.3m) effective section at the support at a free edge may be used to predict the peak shear but, because of torsion, the total reaction due to an edge load will not actually be concentrated in the 1'-0" (0.3m).

Several limitations should be recognized for Figure 3.2.2.

Fig. 3.2.2 Effective resisting width of slab for load anywhere along span

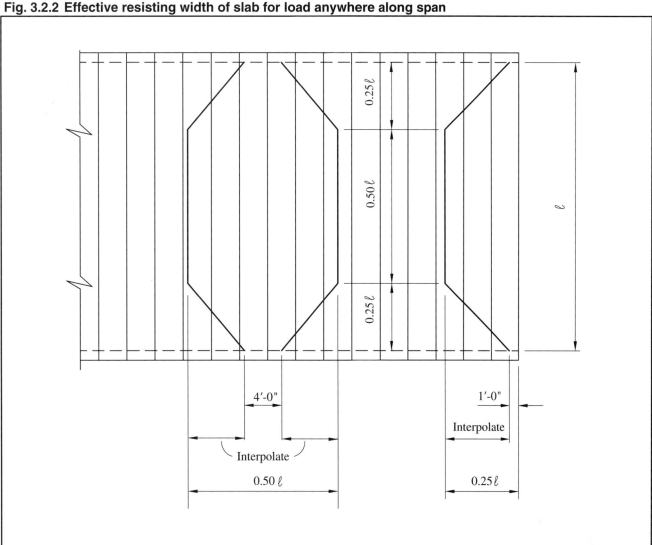

1) As the width of the system becomes narrower than the span length, the effective resisting widths will become narrower.

2) For extremely high span-depth ratios (in excess of approximately 50), the effective section at midspan may be reduced by 10 to 20 percent.

3) For spans less than about 10 ft, the effective width at the support may become narrower.

4) Local load concentrations can cause longitudinal splitting failures due to transverse bending in the system. Punching shear type failures can also occur. The magnitude of concentrated loads must be limited to preclude such failures. These limits are best es-

tablished by test for each slab system. Reference 23 provides guidance for edge loads.

The concept of using an effective resisting section is subtlely different from the traditional concept of load distribution width. Traditionally, loads have been divided by distribution widths for design. Using an effective resisting section means that a given load is resisted by a varying width depending on the location of the section being investigated in the span. This is best illustrated by example.

Example 3.2.1 General Case

Given an untopped hollow core system using 36″ wide slabs as shown in Figure 3.2.3, determine the slab design loads. Slab weight = 53.5 psf

Fig. 3.2.3.

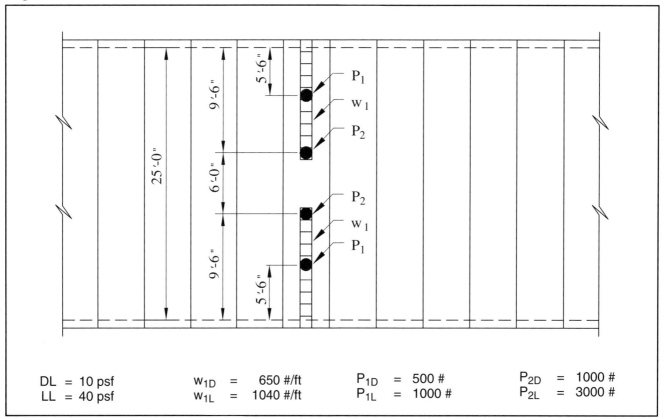

DL = 10 psf	w_{1D} = 650 #/ft	P_{1D} = 500 #	P_{2D} = 1000 #
LL = 40 psf	w_{1L} = 1040 #/ft	P_{1L} = 1000 #	P_{2L} = 3000 #

Solution

Step 1: Evaluate the shear and moment diagrams for the non-distributable loads.

$$w_u = 1.4(53.5 + 10) + 1.7(40) = 157 \text{ psf}$$

$$V_x = w(\ell/2 - x) = 0.157(25/2 - x)$$

$$M_x = w\frac{x}{2}(\ell - x) = \frac{0.157x}{2}(25 - x)$$

See Table 3.2.1

Step 2: Evaluate the shear and moment diagrams for the distributable loads.

$$w_u = 1.4(650) + 1.7(1040) = 2678 \text{ #/ft}$$

$$P_u = 1.4(500) + 1.7(1000) = 2400 \text{ #}$$

$$P_u = 1.4(1000) + 1.7(3000) = 6500 \text{ #}$$

See Table 3.2.1

Step 3: Evaluate the effective width along the span.

At support
DW = 4.0 ft
At $0.25\ell = 0.25(25) = 6.25$ ft

DW $= 0.5\ell = 0.5(25) = 12.5$ ft

Between $x = 0$ and $x = 6.25$ ft
DW $= 4 + \dfrac{x}{6.25}(12.5 - 4)$
$\quad = 4 + 1.36x$
See Table 3.2.1

Step 4: Divide the shears and moments from Step 2 by the effective width from Step 3 and add to the shears and moments in Step 1.

See Table 3.2.1

Step 5: Design the slabs for the web shear, inclined shear, and moments obtained from Step 4.

The solution for the general case where the shears and moments are calculated at intervals along the span is best suited for use with a computer. The information could then also be used to calculate shear strength at the same time.

For many cases, a general solution is not necessary. Simplifying shortcuts can be used to shorten the design process. Consider the case where shear is known not to be a problem.

Table 3.2.1 Shears and Moments for Example 3.2.1

x	Non-distributed Loads V_{ux}	Non-distributed Loads M_{ux}	Distributable Loads V_{ux}	Distributable Loads M_{ux}	Effective Width DW_x	Final V_u(k/ft)	Final M_u(ft-k/ft)
0	1.96	0	34.34	0	4.0	10.55	0
h/2	1.91	0.65	33.45	11.28	4.45	9.43	3.18
1	1.81	1.88	31.66	33.0	5.36	7.72	8.04
2	1.65	3.61	28.98	63.32	6.72	5.96	13.03
3	1.49	5.18	26.31	90.98	8.08	4.75	16.44
4	1.33	6.59	23.63	115.94	9.44	3.83	18.87
5	1.18	7.85	20.95	138.23	10.80	3.12	20.65
6	1.02	8.95	15.87	156.64	12.16	2.32	21.83
7	0.86	9.89	13.19	171.17	12.5	1.92	23.58
10	0.39	11.78	0	195.78	12.5	0.39	27.44
11	0.24	12.09	0	195.78	12.5	0.24	27.75
12.5	0	12.27	0	195.78	12.5	0	27.93

Example 3.2.2

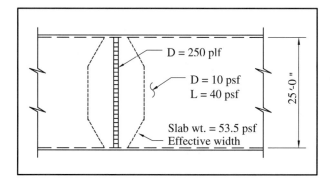

Given the system shown, determine the design load.

Solution:

Shear is judged to be not critical
From Figure 3.2.2 the effective width resisting the line load is $0.50\ell = 0.50(25) = 12.5$ ft

Determine the design superimposed load:

$$w = 40 + 10 + 250/12.5$$

$$= 70 \text{ psf}$$

Using the generic slab load table in Figure 1.7.1 select an 8″ slab with 4 - 7/16″ diameter strands.
If it is not known whether shear is critical, simple iterative checks may be made.

Example 3.2.3

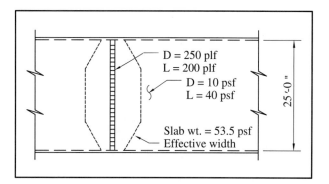

Given the system shown select a generic slab from Figure 1.7.1 to support the loads shown.

Solution:

Make preliminary selection based on flexure:

$$\text{Superimposed } w = 10 + 40 + \frac{(250 + 200)}{(0.50)(25)}$$

$$= 86 \text{ psf}$$

Select 4 - 7/16″, 270 ksi low relaxation strands from Figure 1.7.1

First shear check
effective width at support = 4′-0″ = DW
$$w_u = 1.4(10 + 53.5) + 1.7(40) + (1.4 \times 250 + 1.7 \times 200)/DW$$

$$= 157 + 690/DW$$

Using DW = 4.0

Example 3.2.4

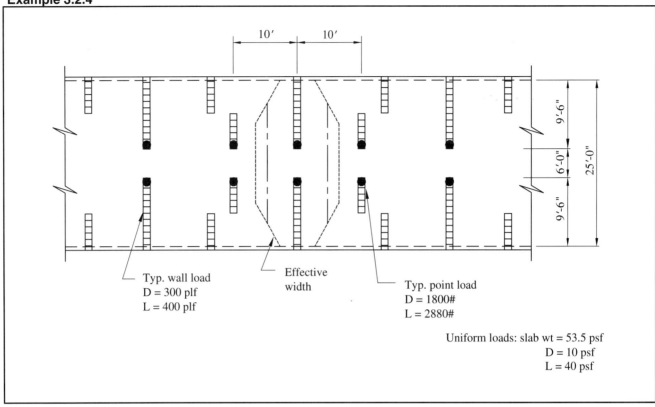

10'   10'

9'-6"
6'-0"
9'-6"
25'-0"

Typ. wall load
D = 300 plf
L = 400 plf

Effective
width

Typ. point load
D = 1800#
L = 2880#

Uniform loads: slab wt = 53.5 psf
D = 10 psf
L = 40 psf

w_u = 157 + 690/4.0 = 330 psf

Check shear based on this load and find
@ h/2 V_u = 4.02 k/ft and ϕV_{cw} = 6.04 k OK

@ 3.0 ft V_u = 3.13 k/ft and ϕV_{ci} = 3.05 k NG

Second Shear Check
Inclined shear did not check at 3.0 ft so determine effective width at 3.0 ft, recalculate distributed load and recheck shear.

At $\ell/4$, DW = 0.5ℓ = 0.5(25) = 12.5 ft
At support, DW = 4.0 ft

Interpolate at 3 ft, DW = $\dfrac{3}{25/4}(12.5 - 4) + 4$

$\qquad\qquad\qquad\quad$ = 8.08 ft

w_u = 157 + 690/DW

$\quad$ = 157 + 690/8.08

$\quad$ = 242 psf

Again check shear at 3.0 ft and beyond and find
$\phi V_{ci} > V_u$ at all points.

Therefore, shear check is complete and slab is adequate.

To summarize the steps taken to check shear in Example 3.2.3, distributable loads were divided by the effective width at the support to make a conservative shear check. If shear along the span is found to be satisfactory, no further steps are required and the shear check is complete. If shear in the span at some point is found to be inadequate, the effective width at that point is used to calculated a new load which will then be conservative for points further into the span. Shear is rechecked. This iterative approach is used until all points further into the span check for shear. If shear works for a given situation, generally no more than three cycles will be required.

A combination of loads will be used to further demonstrate this method in the following example.

Example 3.2.4
Given the center bay of an apartment building as shown, design for the applied loads using the generic slab shown in Figure 1.7.1

Solution:

Select preliminary slab based on flexure:

Use $DW = 0.50\ell = 0.5(25) = 12.5$ ft

Because wall and point loads are spaced closer than 12.5 ft, conservatively use spacing of loads as DW.

At design strip:

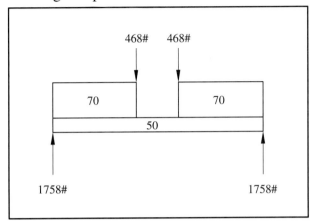

Point loads $= \dfrac{(1800 + 2880)}{10} = 468$ plf

Parallel walls $= \dfrac{(300 + 400)}{10} = 70$ psf

Uniform load $= 10 + 40 = 50$ psf

$M = 11{,}511$ ft-#/ft

equivalent uniform load $= 8 \times 11511/25^2$

$$= 147 \text{ psf}$$

Select 4-$1/2''$, 270 ksi, low relaxation strands capacity = 148 psf at 25 ft.

Check shear
For design strip
including slab wt.

$w_u = 1.4(10 + 53.5)) + 1.7(40)$
    $+ (1.4 \times 300 + 1.7 \times 400)/DW$

$\quad = 157 + 1100/DW$

$P_u = (1.4 \times 1800 + 1.7 \times 2880)/DW$

$\quad = 7416/DW$

Start at support where effective width = 4.0 ft

$w_u = 157 + 1100/4 = 432$ psf

$P_u = 7416/4 = 1854$ plf

Obtain the following results:

x	h/2	1.09'	1.85'	2.61'	3.37'
V_u k/ft	7.11	6.93	6.45	6.12	5.79
ϕV_n k/ft	6.30	7.79	8.44	6.09	4.79

Note that web shear at h/2 does not work. No further modifications can be made to adjust the shear calculation. Shear enhancement is required in the form of stirrups, solid cores, higher concrete strength or using a deeper section.

Proceed to check inclined shear which was not adequate at 2.61 ft.

Recalculate effective width at 2.61 ft as:

$$= \frac{2.61}{0.25\ell}\left(0.5\ell - 4\right) + 4$$

$$= \frac{2.61}{6.25}\left(12.5 - 4\right) + 4 = 7.54'$$

$w_u = 157 + 1100/7.54 = 303$ psf

$P_u = 7416/7.54 = 984$ plf

Obtain the following results:

x	2.61	3.37	4.14	4.90	5.66
V_u k/ft	3.97	3.74	3.51	3.28	3.05
ϕV_n k/ft	6.07	4.77	3.94	3.36	2.94

Inclined shear is now adequate to a distance of 5.66 ft into the span. Recalculate the effective width at 5.66 ft.

$$\frac{5.66}{0.25\ell}\left(0.5\ell - 4\right) + 4$$

$$= 11.7 \text{ ft}$$

Note that loads are located only 10 ft apart which means that design strips would start to overlap. For this case, the maximum effective width might be used as the distance between loads, or 10 feet, rather than 0.5ℓ.

$w_u = 157 + 1100/10 = 267$ psf

$P_u = 7416/10 = 742$ plf

With these loads, it is found that $V_u < \phi V_n$ for the balance of the span. Therefore, the slab selected is adequate except for the shear enhancement required for web shear as previously noted.

3.3 Effect of Openings

Openings may be provided in hollow core systems by saw cutting after a deck is installed and grouted, by shoring and saw cutting, by forming or sawing the openings in the plant or by installing short slabs with steel headers. Some typical header configurations are shown in Section 5.7. In laying out openings for a project, the least structural effect will be obtained by orienting the longest dimension of an opening parallel to a span, or by coring small holes to cut the fewest prestressing strands, or when several openings must be provided, aligning the openings parallel to the span to again cut the least number of prestressing strands.

For slab design, openings cause load concentrations which may be distributed over the slab system as discussed in Section 3.2. As with non-uniform loads, openings cause torsion in the slabs. Therefore, the method of determining shear adequacy must also consider the effects of torsion on the shear stresses. In flexure, the primary considerations are the length of the opening parallel to the span and the length of strand embedment available from the end of an opening to the point of maximum moment.

Figure 3.3.1 shows some general opening locations with suggested interpretations of the effective resisting slab width described in Section 3.2. Local slab producers may have information which would allow different design approaches for their particular slab.

Figure 3.3.1(a) depicts a relatively small opening located at midspan. In flexure, the load from the short slabs can be resisted by slabs within 0.25ℓ on each side of the opening. As a guideline, if an end of the opening shown is not closer to the support than $3/8\ell$, there will be no special considerations for shear design with only uniform loads. When non-uniform loads are superimposed near the opening, the effective resisting section shown in Figure 3.2.2 would then be used for those non-uniform loads.

Figure 3.3.1(b) shows a similar condition where an opening is located with an end closer to the support than $3/8\ell$. In this case, shear is considered as though the opening created a free edge. That is, load from the short slabs or opening will be transmitted as an edge load to the adjacent

Fig. 3.3.1 Effects of openings

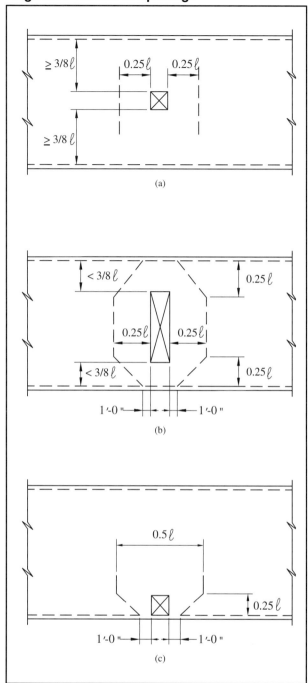

slabs. The resulting torsion on the adjacent slabs requires that a reduced effective width at the support be used if torsional shear stresses are not directly calculated.

Figure 3.3.1(c) depicts the extreme where an opening is located right at the end of a span. Again, the reduced shear width adjacent to the opening is required to reflect torsional shear stresses. An end opening extending less than the lesser of 0.125ℓ or 4 ft (1.2m) into the span may be neglected when considering flexure. However, some capacity reduction might be required for the slab with the opening when strand embedment length is less than full required development. When non-uniform loads are superimposed in the area of an end opening, these loads should be considered as being at a free edge for shear calculations.

Example 3.3.1

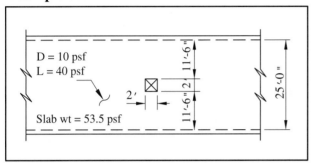

Given the slab system shown, select a generic slab from Figure 1.7.1 to carry the loads given considering the opening.

Solution:

Check proximity of opening to support
$3/8\,\ell = 0.375(25) = 9.38'$

$11.5' > 9.38'$ no special shear considerations

Distribute load from strip with opening:

superimposed $w = 10 + 40 = 50$ psf
load on strip with opening =
$2(10 + 40 + 53.5) = 207$ plf

distributing 1/2 of strip load each side

$$w = 50 + \frac{207/2}{0.25\ell}$$

$$= 50 + \frac{104}{0.25(25)}$$

$$= 67 \text{ psf}$$

Select, from Figure 1.7.1, 4 - $^3/_8''$ dia., 270 ksi, low relaxation strands

Example 3.3.2

Given the floor system shown, select a generic slab from Figure 1.7.1 to carry the loads given.

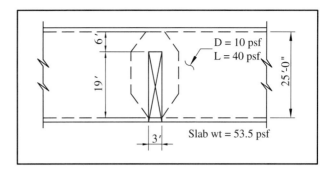

Solution:

The ends of the opening are closer than $3/8\,\ell$ to the support on both ends. Therefore, consider the opening as though it were a free edge.

load on strip with opening
$$w = 3(10 + 40 + 53.5)$$

$$= 311 \text{ plf}$$

for flexure and preliminary slab selection use effective width = $0.25\,\ell$ to each side

$$w = 10 + 40 + \frac{311/2}{0.25(25)}$$

$$= 75 \text{ psf}$$

Try 4 - 7/16″ dia., 270 ksi, low relaxation strands
Check Shear

effective width at support = 1′-0″ each side
$$w_u = 1.4(10 + 53.5) + 1.7(40) +$$

$$\frac{3[1.4(10 + 53.5) + 1.7(40)]/2}{DW}$$

$$= 157 + 235/DW$$

where DW = effective width on each side
$$w_u = 157 + 235/1 = 392 \text{ psf}$$

Using this load, obtain:

x	h/2	1.1	1.85	2.61	3.37	4.14
V_u k/ft	4.77	4.47	4.17	3.87	3.58	3.28
ϕV_n k/ft	6.08	7.29	6.62	4.80	3.80	3.15

Shear is adequate to 4.14 ft into span.
Modify effective width at 4.14 ft

$$DW = \frac{4.14}{0.25\ell}(0.25\ell - 1) + 1$$

$$= \frac{4.14}{6.25}(6.25 - 1) + 1$$

$$= 4.48 \text{ ft}$$

$$w_u = 157 + 235/DW$$

$$= 157 + 235/4.48$$

$$= 209 \text{ psf}$$

Find shear is adequate at 4.14 ft and all points further into span. Use 4 - 7/16″ dia., 270 ksi, low relaxation strands.

3.4 Continuity

Hollow core slabs are normally designed as part of a simple span system. However, continuity over supports can be achieved by placing reinforcing steel in the grouted keyways, in a composite structural topping, or by concreting bars into cores. Within limits, the result will be better control of superimposed load deflections and a lower requirement for positive moment capacity.

With reinforcing steel in either a composite topping or in cores, elastic moments with allowance for negative moment redistribution determine the amount of reinforcing required. Because of the relative efficiencies of positive prestressing steel and negative mild reinforcing, it is difficult to economically justify a continuous system design.

When reinforcing is required at supports for reasons such as structural integrity ties or diaphragm connections, the reinforcing ratios are generally quite low, and therefore, develop little moment capacity. While this reinforcing may be considered in calculating service load deflections, it is recommended that full simple span positive moment capacity be provided for strength design unless moment-curvature relationships existing at the supports at ultimate loads are known.

One situation that seems reasonable for considering a reduction in the positive moment requirements is where the slabs are required to have a fire rating developed using the rational design procedure. In this case, a limit analysis approach would be reasonable.

The negative moment reinforcing, which is unaffected by fire loads, can develop full yield moment potential and effectively provide a plastic hinge at the support. As a result, the positive moment at midspan may be correspondingly reduced. A detailed discussion of this is presented in Section 6.3.3.

3.5 Cantilevers

Cantilever design in hollow core slabs differs from design with conventional precast members because of the production procedures used for hollow core slabs. Guidelines noted here are conservative and may be exceeded depending on the specific product used.

Because long line beds are used for the production of hollow core slabs, top prestressing strands may be economical only when full bed capacity is utilized. Even then, substantial amounts of prestressing strand may be used inefficiently because of debonding requirements. The economics of using top strand must, therefore, be determined by the local producer.

When top strands are used, the length of the cantilever is usually not sufficient to fully develop a strand. A reduced value for f_{ps} is required and the design procedures given in Section 2.6 should be used. In dry cast systems, the bond of top strands may be less than desired so a further reduction in f_{ps} is required. This reduction may be substantial and each producer should be consulted on top strand bond performance.

When top strands are not economical, non-prestressed reinforcement may be placed in the cores or directly in the unit in the case of a wet cast product. This is generally done while the slab concrete is still plastic so bond of the fill concrete with the slab may be achieved. The reinforcement is selected based on conventional design with due consideration given to bar development length.

With either top strands or reinforcing bars, it may be necessary to debond portions of the bottom prestressing strand in the cantilever zone to help minimize the top tension under service loads. Not all producers have the ability to debond bottom strands which could potentially limit cantilever length or load capacity.

It is desirable to limit service level tensions in cantilevers so that uncracked section properties may be used to more accurately predict deflections. The tensile stress limit may vary for different systems used. For example, the practice with some dry cast systems is to limit tensile stresses to 100 psi (0.7 MPa). In other dry cast systems and in wet cast systems, the limit may be raised to $6\sqrt{f'_c}$. The tension limit will basically be a function of a producer's past experience.

As a rule of thumb, cantilever lengths falling in the range of 6 to 12 times the slab thickness will be workable depending on the superimposed load and individual producer's capabilities.

Example 3.5.1 Cantilever Design

Using the generic hollow core slab section defined in Section 1.7, design for the following conditions shown in Figure 3.5.1.

Fig. 3.5.1

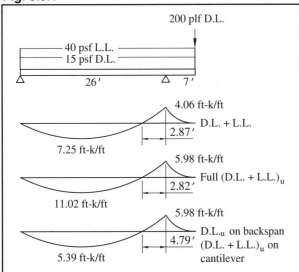

Solution:

From the load table in Figure 1.7.1, select 4 - $^3/_8''$ dia., 270 ksi strands as the primary reinforcement. Try 2 - $^3/_8''$ dia., 270 ksi, low relaxation strands as cantilever reinforcement. Assume 15% losses and 70% initial stress.

Check stresses at cantilever:

Bottom strands:

$$f_{top} = 0.7(0.85)(4)(23)\left(\frac{1}{154} - \frac{2.89 \times 4.11}{1224.5}\right)$$

$$= -0.176 \text{ ksi (tension)}$$

Top strands:

$$f_{top} = 0.7(0.85)(2)(23)\left(\frac{1}{154} - \frac{3.11 \times 4.11}{1224.5}\right)$$

$$= +0.463 \text{ ksi}$$

Applied moment:

$$f_{top} = -\frac{4.06(3)(12)(4.11)}{1224.5}$$

$$= -0.491 \text{ ksi (tension)}$$

Net tension with fully bonded bottom strands:

$$f_t = -0.176 + 0.463 - 0.491$$

$$= -0.204 \text{ ksi}$$

Allow $6\sqrt{5000} = 0.424$ ksi OK

Note that some of the bottom strands could have been debonded for the length of the cantilever if top tensile stresses had exceeded a desirable level.

Stresses in backspan:

Because the backspan is long in this example, stresses will not be critical in the backspan. When the backspan is short relative to the cantilever length, stresses may require a check in the backspan to determine the length of bonding of the top strands.

Ultimate Strength

At the cantilever, strain compatibility will generally show that the bottom strands may be ignored in determining the nominal moment capacity. When the bottom prestress is very heavy or the bottom strands are high in the slab, a strain compatibility analysis should be performed considering both strand layers.

For this example, assume the bottom strands may be ignored.

$$f_{ps} = 270\left[1 - \left(\frac{0.28}{0.8}\right)\left(\frac{2(0.085)(270)}{(36)(7)(5)}\right)\right]$$

$$= 265 \text{ ksi}$$

$$a = \frac{2(0.085)(265)}{(0.85)(5)(36)} = 0.294 \text{ in}$$

$$\phi M_n = \frac{0.9}{12}(2)(0.085)(265)\left(7 - \frac{0.294}{2}\right)$$

$$= 23.15 \text{ ft-k/slab}$$

$$M_u = 3(5.98) = 17.94 \text{ ft-k/slab}$$

$$M_{cr} = \frac{1224.5}{4.11}\left(0.463 - 0.176 + \frac{7.5\sqrt{5000}}{1000}\right)\frac{1}{12}$$

$$= 20.29 \text{ ft-k/slab}$$

$$\frac{\phi M_n}{M_{cr}} = \frac{23.15}{20.29} = 1.14 < 1.2 \text{ NG}$$

Add 1 - #4 bar top per slab.

Design summary

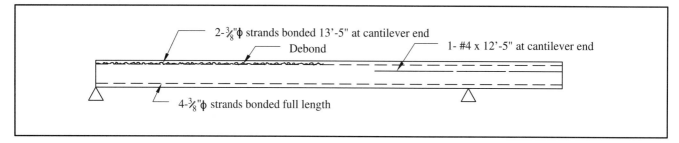

Check length of top strand to be bonded:

$$l_{available} = 7(12) = 84 \text{ in}$$

$$\ell_d = (f_{ps} - 2/3f_{se})d_b$$

$$= (265 - 2(0.7)(0.85)(270)/3)(0.375)$$

$$= 59.2 \text{ in} < 84 \text{ in}$$

Therefore, the strand is fully effective in the cantilever. The moment capacity would have to be recalculated by the procedures of Section 2.6 if the development length were found to be greater than the length available.

Bond of the top strands in the backspan must be long enough to develop the f_{ps} required in the cantilever design. The top strands should also be bonded for a distance of one transfer length (50 diameters) past the inflection point under the worst load condition. For this example a bonded length of 77 in. would be required.

Alternate Design

Provide mild reinforcement in lieu of top prestressing strands

Try 2 - #5 Gr 60 bars at d = 7″

$$a = \frac{2(0.31)(60)}{(0.85)(5)(36)} = 0.243″$$

$$\phi M_n = \frac{0.9}{12}(2)(0.31)(60)\left(7 - \frac{0.243}{2}\right)$$

$$= 19.19 \text{ ft-k/slab}$$

$$= 6.4 \text{ ft-k/ft} > 5.98 \quad \text{OK}$$

Top stress $= -0.176 - 0.491$

$$= -0.667 \text{ ksi with fully bonded bottom strands}$$

Note that a cracked section must be considered in calculating cantilever deflections because the top stress exceeds a tension of $6\sqrt{f'_c}$.

3.6 Horizontal Joints

Figure 3.6.1 depicts three conditions typically used in a multistory wall bearing building where hollow core slabs are used in a platform detail. Several expressions [27-31] have been proposed to describe the transfer of axial load through this horizontal joint.

With hollow core slabs used for floors, the most efficient detail is to build the slab ends into the wall. Depending on the butt joint size, the strength of the joint for transfer of vertical loads can be enhanced with the addition of grout in the butt joint, Fig. 3.6.1(b), and in both the joint and cores, Fig. 3.6.1(c). Grout fill in the cores increases the net slab width and provides confinement for a grout column.

The strength of the joint for vertical load transfer can be predicted using Eq. 3.6.1 for an ungrouted joint, Fig. 3.6.1(a). For a grouted joint, Fig. 3.6.1(b) or (c), the greater of Eq. 3.6.1 and Eq. 3.6.2 can be used. Both grouted and ungrouted joints can have the slab cores either filled or not filled. Both equations include a capacity reduction term for load eccentric from the centerline of the joint. With single story walls braced at the top and bottom, this eccentricity will be negligible.

$$\phi P_n = \phi 0.85 A_e f'_c R_e \qquad \text{(Eq. 3.6.1)}$$

$$\phi P_n = \phi t_g \ell f_u C R_e / k \qquad \text{(Eq. 3.6.2)}$$

where

P_n = nominal strength of the joint

A_e = effective bearing area of slab in joint = $2wb_w$

w = bearing strip width

b_w = net web width of slab when cores are not filled

= unit width as solid slab when cores are filled

f'_c = design compressive strength of slab concrete or grout whichever is less

t_g = grout column thickness

Fig. 3.6.1 Common platform details

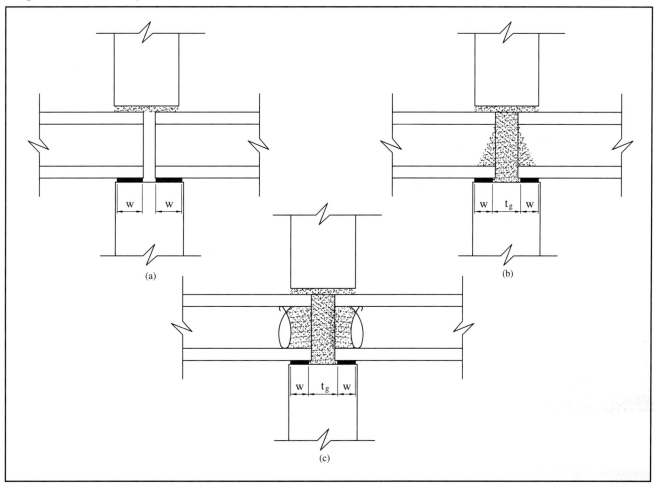

(a)

(b)

(c)

ℓ = width of slab being considered

f_u = design compressive strength of wall or grout whichever is less when walls are reinforced against splitting and slab cores are filled

= 80% of design compressive strength of wall or design compressive strength of grout, whichever is less when walls are not reinforced against splitting or slab cores are not filled

C = 1.0 when cores are not filled

= $1.4\sqrt{2500/f'_c(\text{grout})} \geq 1.0$ when cores are filled

k = $0.65 + (f'_c(\text{grout}) - 2500)/50{,}000$

R_e = reduction factor for eccentricity of load

= $1 - 2e/h$

e = eccentricity of applied load measured from joint centerline

h = wall thickness

ϕ = 0.7

Where bearing strips with a modulus of elasticity other than 50,000 psi (345 MPa) are used, the amount of force in the grout column will be altered. A theoretical approach presented in Reference 30 considers pad stiffness, grout column strength as compared to grout strength, and confinement of the grout column. A comparison of this theoretical procedure with the Johal procedure indicates that conservative capacity will be predicted by substituting the actual pad modulus of elasticity for 50,000 when calculating k.

The bearing strips need to also be checked against manufacturer's recommended stress limits. Figure 3.6.2 summarizes the forces in the joint and the recommended effective bearing strip width.

Another set of forces acting on the horizontal joint develop from the negative moments induced in the floor slabs due to the clamping effect of a bearing wall on the slab ends. Two consequences

Fig. 3.6.2. Force distribution in horizontal joint

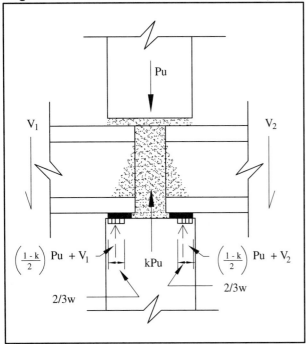

result. The splitting strength of the bearing wall is reduced when the normal force restraining slab end rotation is considered. Secondly, the joint or slab may crack to relieve the frictional restraint. This condition is undesirable from either the standpoint of joint or slab integrity. Reinforcing normal to the slab butt joint is most efficient for controlling this condition. To date, there are no published studies to evaluate effects of this rotational restraint. No adverse effects have been cited when nominal diaphragm or structural integrity reinforcement has been provided across the joint.

Example 3.6.1

Using the generic hollow core slab section defined in Section 1.7, determine the grouting requirements for an interior butt joint as depicted in Figure 3.6.1(a) given the following criteria:

Slab span: 28 feet
18 story building with:
    8″ concrete bearing walls
    f'_c wall = 5000 psi

Loads: Roof – DL = 15 psf LL = 30 psf

         Floors – DL = 10 psf LL = 40 psf

         Walls – DL = 800 plf/story

LL Reduction: None for example

Solution:
Loads
  Roof: w_u = 28 (1.4(53.5+15)+1.7(30))
           = 4.11 klf

  Floors: w_u = 28 (1.4(53.5+10)+1.7(40))
           = 4.39 klf

  Walls: w_u = 1.4(800)
           = 1.12 klf/story

Accumulate loads above floor noted

Floor	w_u	Σw_u
18	4.11 + 1.12	5.23
17	4.39 + 1.12	10.74
16	5.51	16.25
15	5.51	21.76
14	5.51	27.27
13	5.51	32.78
12	5.51	38.29
11	5.51	43.80
10	5.51	49.31
9	5.51	54.82
8	5.51	60.33
7	5.51	65.84
6	5.51	71.35
5	5.51	76.86
4	5.51	82.37
3	5.51	87.88
2	5.51	93.39

a) Evaluate capacity of ungrouted joint (Fig. 3.6.1(a))

b_w = 10.5″ for generic slab = 3.5 in/ft of width

f'_c (slab) = 5000 psi

3 in bearing strips

$$\phi P_n = \phi 0.85 \, A_e \, f'_c \, R_e \qquad \text{(Eq. 3.6.1)}$$

$$\phi P_n = 0.7(0.85)(2)(3)(3.5)(5)\left[1 - \frac{2(0)}{8}\right]$$

$$= 62.48 \text{ k/ft}$$

Adequate for Floors 8 through roof

b) Evaluate strength of grouted joint using 3000 psi grout for

1) 2 in butt joint with no filled cores (Fig. 3.6.1(b))

$$\phi P_n = \phi\, 0.85 A_e f'_c R_e \qquad \text{(Eq. 3.6.1)}$$

$$= 0.7(0.85)(2)(3)(3.5)(5)\left(1 - \frac{2(0)}{8}\right)$$

$$= 62.48 \text{ k/ft}$$

or

$$\phi P_n = \phi t_g \ell f_u C R_e / k \qquad \text{(Eq. 3.6.2)}$$

$$f_u = 3000 \text{ psi}$$

$$C = 1.0$$

$$k = 0.65 + (3000 - 2500)/5000$$

$$= 0.66$$

$$\phi P_n = 0.7(2)(12)(3)(1.0)$$

$$\qquad \text{x}\left(1 - \frac{2(0)}{8}\right)/0.66$$

$$= 76.36 \text{ k/ft} > 62.48$$

Therefore $\phi P_n = 76.36$ k/ft

2) $^1/_2$ in butt joint with cores filled (Fig. 3.6.1(c))

$$\phi P_n = \phi\, 0.85 A_e f'_c R_e \qquad \text{(Eq. 3.6.1)}$$

$$= 0.7(0.85)(2)(3)(12)(3)\left(1 - \frac{2(0)}{8}\right)$$

$$= 128.5 \text{ k/ft}$$

or

$$\phi P_n = \phi t_g \ell f_u C R_e / k \qquad \text{(Eq. 3.6.2)}$$

$$f_u = 3000 \text{ psi}$$

$$C = 1.4\sqrt{2500/3000} = 1.28$$

$$k = 0.65 + (3000 - 2500)/50,000 = 0.66$$

$$\phi P_n = 0.7(0.5)(12)(3)(1.28)$$

$$\qquad \text{x}\left(1 - \frac{2(0)}{8}\right)/0.66$$

$$= 24.4 \text{ k/ft} < 128.5$$

Therefore $\phi P_n = 128.5$ k/ft

Use 1/2 in butt joint with cores filled below 8th floor.

It should be noted that this example may overstate the height of building that can be supported on an ungrouted joint. Concentrated loads due to corridor lintels, wall openings, or exterior spandrels must also be considered in most buildings resulting in an increase in load to be transferred through the horizontal joint.

CHAPTER 4

DIAPHRAGM ACTION WITH HOLLOW CORE SLABS

4.1 General Information

When hollow core slabs are used as floor or roof decks to support vertical loads, the natural extension is to use the slabs as a diaphragm to resist and transmit lateral loads. Lateral loads will be applied to building structures in the form of lateral earth pressures, wind loads or seismic loads. The function of a diaphragm is to receive these loads from the building elements to which they have been applied and transmit the loads to the lateral-resisting elements which carry the lateral loads to the foundation. The design issues in a hollow core diaphragm are the design of connections to get loads into the diaphragm, the strength and ductility of the slab system to transmit these loads to the lateral-resisting elements and the design of the connections required to unload the lateral forces from the diaphragm to the lateral-resisting elements.

Clear communication is required between the building designer and the hollow core slab supplier when the hollow core system is to be used as a diaphragm. Some elements of the diaphragm design may be delegated to the hollow core slab supplier. However, only the building designer is in the position to know all the parameters involved in generating the applied lateral loads. Because of many design issues, only the building designer can determine the location and relative stiffnesses of the lateral-resisting elements. These parameters dictate the distribution of forces in the diaphragm. If any design responsibility will be delegated to the hollow core supplier, the location and magnitude of the lateral loads applied to the diaphragm and the location and magnitude of forces to be transmitted to lateral-resisting elements must be specified. Where hollow core slabs must connect to other building materials, or where demands on connections go beyond simple strength demands, the connection details should be shown in the contract documents.

An additional consideration in detailing diaphragms is the need for structural integrity. ACI Section 16.5 provides minimum requirements to satisfy Section 7.13 in precast concrete structures. For large panel bearing wall structures, minimum forces are specified to provide ties throughout the structure. For other types of precast structures, only general detailing philosophies are specified. In either case, the fundamental requirement is to provide a complete load path from any point in a structure to the foundation. Clearly, a diaphragm is a significant element in this load path. A tie system that satisfies the strength and force transfer demands on a diaphragm will generally satisfy the detailing requirements for structural integrity.

4.2 Design Loads

Lateral loads imposed on hollow core diaphragms can include lateral earth pressures, wind loads or seismic loads. Lateral earth pressures will be established by the characteristics of the soil being retained. Wind and seismic loads will be dictated by the applicable building code for the structure. Soil and wind loads are forces actually applied to the structure. Seismic forces are generated from within the structure as inertial forces due to lateral displacement from ground motions. While soil and wind loads can be safely treated as static loads, seismic loads must be considered as dynamic loads. In all cases, the same elements will comprise a complete diaphragm, but the ductility demands on a seismic resistant system are significantly more important.

The balance of the discussion in this chapter will be concerned with lateral loads from wind and seismic. This is not intended to slight the importance of considering unbalanced soil pressures which can commonly be a significant consideration in many projects using hollow core slabs. The basic principles of hollow core diaphragms which will be discussed are equally applicable to lateral soil pressures.

There are many documents which cover design for wind and seismic loads. The references used for this chapter are the 1994 UBC code[32] and the 1996 BOCA code[33]. For wind load, both codes are similar in that a basic wind speed is selected based on the building location, an exposure category is selected based on the surrounding terrain, an importance factor is selected based on the occupancy of the building, modifying factors are determined for the geometry of the building and the design positive and negative wind pressures are calculated.

For seismic loads, the two codes take different approaches. The UBC code allows an equivalent static load approach for many building types. For others, where certain heights or irregularities are present, a dynamic lateral force procedure is required. The static force procedure allows design for a base shear of:

$$V = \frac{ZIC}{R_w}W \qquad \text{(Eq. 4.2.1)}$$

where

Z = seismic zone factor

I = importance factor

C = factor dependent on site and structure fundamental period

R_w = coefficient dependent on structural system type

W = total dead load plus other applicable loads

This base shear is then distributed over the height of the structure in proportion to the distribution of weights over the height. Additionally, a minimum eccentricity of 5% of the building dimension perpendicular to the direction being considered shall be included when determining the distribution of forces to the lateral-resisting elements when the diaphragm is not flexible. Specific to diaphragms, for Zones 2, 3, and 4, the UBC requires that a floor or roof diaphragm resist a force equal to:

$$F_{px} = \frac{F_t + \sum\limits_{i=x}^{n} F_i}{\sum\limits_{i=x}^{n} w_i} w_{px} \qquad \text{(Eq. 4.2.2)}$$

where

F_{px} = force applied to diaphragm at level under consideration

F_t = additional portion of base shear applied at top level

F_i = portion of base shear applied at level i

w_i = portion of W at level i

w_{px} = portion of W at level under consideration

The magnitude of F_{px} need not exceed $0.75ZIw_{px}$ but shall not be less than $0.35\ ZIw_{px}$. Many other requirements are included in the UBC code which are not restated in this summary.

The BOCA code prescribes a seismic design procedure. A very important note is that the BOCA provisions result in forces that are already factored and are intended to be used with ultimate strength design methods with no additional load factors. The base shear is calculated as:

$$V = C_sW \qquad \text{(Eq. 4.2.3.)}$$

where

C_s = coefficient related to peak velocity-related acceleration, soil profile, structural system type and building fundamental period

W = total dead load plus other applicable loads

The base shear is distributed over the height of the building in proportion to the distribution of the building mass with consideration of the building period. A minimum eccentricity of 5% of the perpendicular building dimension is also required by BOCA when distributing forces to the lateral-resisting elements. For Seismic Performance Categories B and greater, each floor or roof diaphragm shall be designed for a minimum load equal to 50% of the effective peak velocity-related acceleration times the weight attributable to the level under consideration. The peak velocity-related acceleration is determined by the project location. Again, there are many provisions in the BOCA code which are not covered in this summary.

In light of the performance of some diaphragms in recent earthquakes, the seismic demand on diaphragms is an area of new focus. Preliminary indications are that diaphragms should remain elastic during a seismic event to ensure that post-elastic behavior can be achieved in the lateral-resisting elements. By designing a diaphragm to remain elastic, several things are accomplished. Diaphragm flexibility, discussed in Section 4.3 will be less significant. The ductility requirements for connection details will be of less concern. The horizontal distribution of forces to lateral-resisting elements can be maintained.

The building code provisions summarized above are based on achieving post-elastic performance. To keep a diaphragm compatible with

Fig. 4.3.1 Diaphragm bending moments

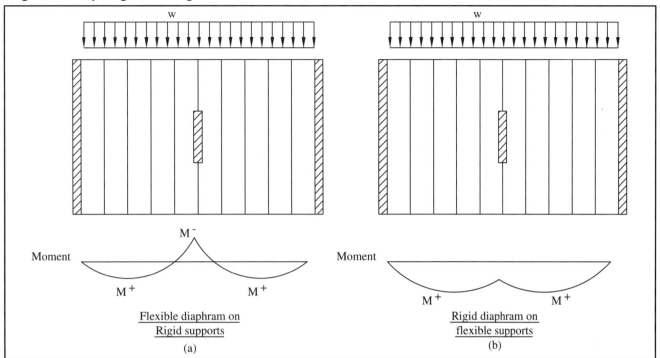

Flexible diaphram on
Rigid supports

(a)

Rigid diaphram on
flexible supports

(b)

post-elastic performance in the lateral-resisting system system, an analysis can be done to evaluate the total potential post-elastic capacity of the lateral-resisting elements. Providing a diaphragm with strength beyond this capacity will achieve compatibility, but will involve significant analysis. Alternatively, the diaphragm design forces prescribed by the building codes can be increased by a factor of 2R/5 to keep the diaphragm elastic and minimize required analysis. Whether building code provisions are based on service or factored load levels, use of 2R/5 loads will result in factored loads for design.

4.3 Distribution of Lateral Forces

Once the lateral forces to be applied to the diaphragm have been determined, the next problem is to determine the distribution of those lateral forces to the lateral-resisting elements which will carry the forces to the foundation. This problem is usually structurally indeterminate which means that deformation compatibilities must be considered for establishing equilibrium. The stiffnesses to be considered are those of the diaphragm and the lateral-resisting elements. Concrete diaphragms are normally considered to be rigid when compared to the lateral-resisting elements. Depending on the type and magnitude of lateral forces applied, a hollow core diaphragm may need

to be considered as a flexible diaphragm. Analysis considering flexible diaphragms is much more complex than for rigid diaphragms and should be considered in light of the project complexity and seismicity for the project location. For most low and mid-rise structures in low seismic risk areas, an assumption of a rigid diaphragm will be reasonable.

The difference in behavior of flexible and rigid diaphragms is illustrated in Figure 4.3.1. In (a), the flexible diaphragm with rigid supports behaves as a continuous beam. Shears and moments in the diaphragm are a function of the plan geometry. In (b), the deflections of the flexible supports must be the same because of the rigid diaphragm. The diaphragm shears and moments will be a function of the relative stiffnesses of the supports. The differences between (a) and (b) can be considerable. Actual behavior will fall between the two cases tending toward one or the other as a function of the diaphragm stiffness.

In seismic areas, the topic of diaphragm flexibility has become a more significant issue. UBC requires consideration of the diaphragm flexibility for the horizontal distribution of forces. A flexible diaphragm is defined by the UBC as one having a maximum lateral deformation more than twice the average story drift for the level under consideration. It may be inferred from UBC Section 1631.1 that this consideration would only apply in seismic zones 2, 3, and 4. The BOCA code simply states that the horizontal distribution of forces consider the relative stiffnesses of the lateral-resisting system and the diaphragm. This provision would apply to Seismic Performance Categories B and greater. By code then, diaphragm flexibility need not be considered when designing for wind or for seismic loads in Zones 0 and 1 under the UBC or Seismic Performance Category A under BOCA.

When diaphragm flexibility must be considered, a cracked moment of inertia calculation is suggested in Reference 34 and a Virendeel truss model in suggested in Reference 35. Since the analysis of a structure with a flexible diaphragm is dependent on so many factors beyond the diaphragm itself, such analysis is beyond the scope of this manual.

4.4 Structural Integrity

As noted in the introduction to this chapter, the ACI code requires consideration of structural integrity for all precast concrete structures. While proper detailing for lateral loads will satisfy the complete load path philosophy of structural integrity, there are some minimum provisions in ACI Section 16.5 which must be met. With specific regard to diaphragms, provisions to be aware of include:

1. For buildings other than large panel bearing wall buildings, the connection to the diaphragm of members being laterally braced by the diaphragm shall have a minimum nominal tensile strength of 300 lb per lin ft (4.4KN/m).

2. For large panel bearing wall structures, a summary of the tie forces is given in Figure 4.4.1 and are required to have the following minimum nominal strengths:

T_1 = nominal strength of 1500 lb per lin ft (21.9 KN/m) of floor or roof span

T_2 = nominal strength of 16,000 lb (71 KN)

T_3 = nominal strength of 1500 lb per lin ft (21.9 KN/m) of wall

These minimum strengths shall not control if the actual forces in the diaphragm are greater.

Fig. 4.4.1 Tie forces in bearing wall buildings

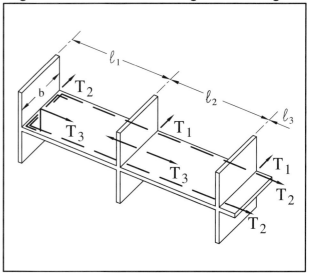

For seismic loading, it is preferable to use conventional reinforcing steel for these types of ties to limit the elongations and deformations. When structural integrity requirements control in nonseismic areas, untensioned prestressing strands may be used to satisfy the strength requirements.

4.5 Elements of a Diaphragm

Figure 4.5.1 illustrates the various elements which comprise a complete diaphragm. The following definitions will be used to describe the various elements:

Boundary Element: Edge member around the perimeter of a diaphragm or the perimeter of an opening in a diaphragm which ties the diaphragm together. The boundary element may function as a chord or a drag strut.

Collector: Elements which transfer shear from the diaphragm to a lateral-resisting element.

Chord: Tension or compression element creating a flange for the diaphragm to develop flexural integrity in the diaphragm.

Drag Strut: Element used to "drag" lateral loads into the lateral-resisting elements and to distribute shears over a greater length of the diaphragm web. (Also called diaphragm strut.)

Longitudinal joint: Joint oriented parallel to the slab span.

Transverse joint: Joint oriented perpendicular to the slab span.

To satisfy structural integrity, all diaphragms should have boundary elements of some type. The boundary elements are essential to ensure that a diaphragm will have the strength to transfer lateral loads to the lateral-resisting system. As a chord, tension reinforcement is placed in the boundary element to allow the diaphragm to act as a deep horizontal beam or tied arch. This reinforcement can also provide shear friction steel for shear transfer along the longitudinal joints.

Collectors are required in all diaphragms to transfer forces from the diaphragm to the lateral-resisting elements. Such connectors are also required for structural integrity to provide a complete load path for lateral forces to the foundation. Collectors may also function to get forces into a diaphragm.

Drag struts act to engage a longer length of diaphragm web for transferring diaphragm shears into the lateral-resisting elements. A drag strut is parallel to the applied load, receives load from the diaphragm and transfers load to the lateral-resisting element as an axial tension or compression. Drag struts are not required for structural integrity as long as the diaphragm is connected directly to the lateral-resisting elements. Drag struts simply spread out shears that might otherwise be highly localized. Under the UBC code, it is implied that drag struts are required elements in Zones 2, 3, and 4. The BOCA code is silent on the use of drag struts, but it can be implied that they are required for Seismic Performance Categories B and greater.

When a bonded structural topping is used with a hollow core slab diaphragm, these elements can be provided directly by reinforcement in the topping. When no topping is provided, these elements are developed as grouted or concrete elements external to the hollow core slabs. As a simple example, Figure 4.5.2 depicts two common boundary conditions. In (a), the boundary reinforcement is placed in a masonry bond beam and the collector reinforcement is placed in the keyways between slabs. In (b), the boundary reinforcement is placed in a grouted or concrete filled space at the end of the slabs. The collector reinforcement is again placed in the keyways between slabs. The primary difference between the details is that the boundary reinforcement in (a) is eccentric from the diaphragm web while it is concentric

Fig. 4.5.1 Diaphragm elements

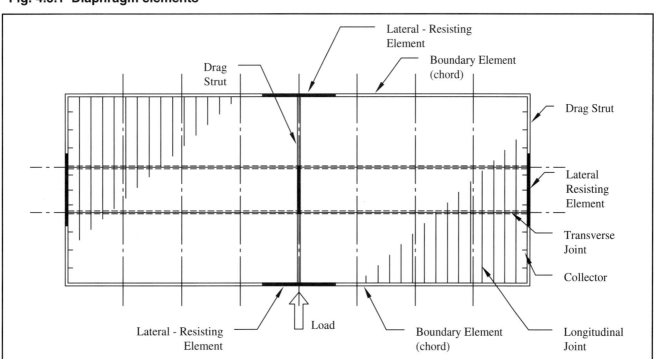

Fig. 4.5.2 Boundary elements

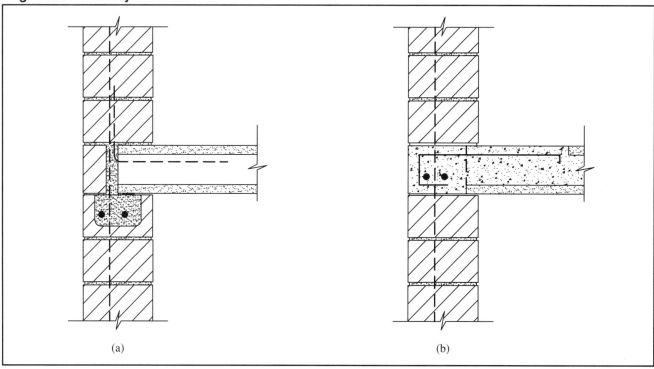

(a)   (b)

in (b). The concentric boundary element will exhibit better performance in a seismic situation and should be used in Zones 3 and 4 under the UBC or Seismic Performance Categories C, D and E under the BOCA code.

4.6 Diaphragm Strength

The diaphragm must have the strength to transfer imposed lateral loads from the point of application to the point of resistance. The diaphragm spans between lateral-resisting elements as a deep beam or tied arch. Shears and tensions will develop and must be resisted in the diaphragm to have a complete system.

4.6.1 Longitudinal Joints

The grouted keyways between slabs do have capacity to transfer longitudinal shear from one slab to the next. Using a shear stress of 80 psi (0.55 MPa), the useable ultimate strength for longitudinal shear is:

$$\phi V_n = \phi(0.08)h_n \ell \qquad \text{(Eq. 4.6.1)}$$

where

ℓ = length of joint under consideration (in)

h_n = net height of grout key (in)

ϕ = 0.85

Fig. 4.6.1 Shear friction steel in butt joint

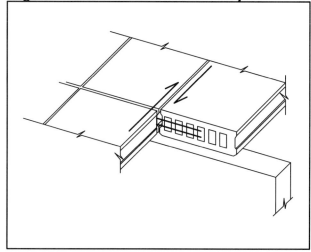

When the grout strength is exceeded or ductile behavior is required, shear friction principles may be used to design reinforcement to be placed perpendicular to the longitudinal joints.[36] This reinforcement may be placed in the transverse joints at the slab ends rather than being distributed along the length of the joints. Placed as shown in Figure 4.6.1, the area of steel is calculated as:

$$A_{vf} = \frac{V_u}{\phi f_y \mu} \qquad \text{(Eq. 4.6.2)}$$

where

V_u = factored applied shear

Fig. 4.6.2 Alternate longitudinal shear connections

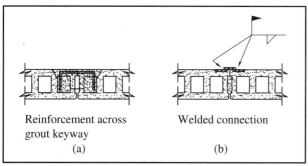

Reinforcement across grout keyway
(a)

Welded connection
(b)

μ = 1.0 for shear parallel to longitudinal joints

= 1.4 for shear parallel to transverse joints where concrete can flow into cores

ϕ = 0.85

While the detail shown in Figure 4.6.1 is the most economical means of providing a mechanical connection across the longitudinal joints, alternate connections are available which may be desirable in certain circumstances. Figure 4.6.2(a) shows reinforcing steel placed across the longitudinal joint and grouted into the cores. This detail might be considered when the amount of reinforcement required in the transverse joints is great enough to cause congestion. Figure 4.6.2(b) shows weld anchors in the slabs and a loose plate welded across the longitudinal joint. Use of this detail should be carefully coordinated with the hollow core slab supplier to ensure that proper anchorage of the weld plates in the slabs can be accomplished.

Where the diaphragm must unload shear into a lateral-resisting element, boundary element or interior drag strut, a condition similar to the longitudinal joint exists. For longitudinal shear, again shear friction can be used to design reinforcement as the collector to cross potential crack planes and transfer the shear. Figure 4.6.3 depicts an example of such a collector detail. While drag struts and boundary elements may have a vertical stiffness similar to the slab deck, the lateral-resisting elements will usually have a significantly higher vertical stiffness. The collectors connecting directly to the lateral-resisting elements will tend to be rigid vertically. While strength and toughness at such collectors is certainly important, it is equally important to consider every day performance of the structure. At rigid vertical elements, it may be desirable to allow slab camber growth or

Fig. 4.6.3 Collector detail

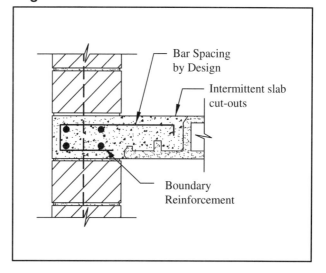

Bar Spacing by Design

Intermittent slab cut-outs

Boundary Reinforcement

Fig. 4.6.4 Potential effects of rigid lap connection

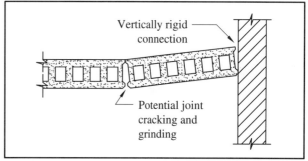

Vertically rigid connection

Potential joint cracking and grinding

deflection to occur without distress at the connection. Figure 4.6.4 shows potential damage at the first interior longitudinal joint when a vertically rigid connection is used. The potential for distress is dependent on the slab span and the real applied loads. Short, lightly loaded spans may experience no problems.

The effect of different vertical stiffnesses may be accounted for by:

1. Determining that distress will not affect the strength or performance of the system,

2. Locating vertically rigid connections near the slab supports where vertical movement is minimized, or

3. Providing allowance for vertical movement in the connection detail.

4.6.2 Transverse Joints

The transverse joints serve many functions. As described in Section 4.6.1, reinforcement in the transverse joints may provide the shear friction reinforcement for shear in the longitudinal joints. The transverse joint may also have to act as a drag strut with axial tension or compression to carry diaphragm loads to the lateral-resisting elements. A transverse joint may also be the chord member where flexural tension is resisted. Finally, an interior transverse joint disrupts the web of the horizontal beam where horizontal shear would have to be transferred to maintain the composite depth of the diaphragm.

The design of shear friction reinforcement for longitudinal joint shear is covered in Section 4.6.1. Drag strut reinforcement is calculated simply as:

$$A_s = \frac{T_u}{\phi f_y} \qquad \text{(Eq. 4.6.3)}$$

Chord tension is resisted by reinforcement to provide flexural strength to the diaphragm. It is suggested that the effective depth of the reinforcement from the compression side of the diaphragm be limited to 0.8 times the depth of the diaphragm. Hence, the chord reinforcement is calculated as:

$$A_s = \frac{M_u}{\phi 0.8 h f_y} \qquad \text{(Eq. 4.6.4)}$$

where

h = depth of the diaphragm

ϕ = 0.9

Because diaphragms tend to act as tied arches rather than beams, tension in the chord reinforcement does not go to zero at the ends of the diaphragm. The chord reinforcement must be anchored at the ends of the diaphragm where a standard hook at the corner will suffice. For horizontal shear in the web of the diaphragm, a shear parallel to the transverse joint is developed. Shear friction reinforcement perpendicular to the transverse joint and embedded in the slab keyways can be used to reinforce for this shear. The applied shear can be calculated as:

$$V_h = \frac{V_u Q}{I}$$

or

$$V_h = \frac{M_u}{jh} \qquad \text{(Eq. 4.6.5)}$$

In the first case, a unit shear is calculated and shear friction reinforcement is distributed according to the shear diagram. In the second case, the total shear is calculated as the tension or compression of the internal couple. In this case, shear friction reinforcement is uniformly distributed over the length between zero moment and maximum moment. It is suggested that the shear friction reinforcement be distributed according to the shear diagram in UBC zones 3 and 4 and BOCA Seismic Performance Categories C, D and E to minimize the force redistribution required with a uniform spacing.

Because of the orientation of the joints and the loading directions considered, the reinforcement in the transverse joint discussed above is not all additive. Typically, the chord tension and longitudinal joint shear will be concurrent. The drag strut tension will typically occur with loads applied in the perpendicular direction.

4.7 Collectors

Collectors function as connections to transfer forces into diaphragms and from diaphragms to boundary elements, drag struts or lateral-resisting elements. The preceding discussion has indicated that reinforcing bars may be used as collectors using shear friction design procedures. As shear friction reinforcement, the steel is used in tension to resist a shear force. In detailing the steel, a crack plane is defined and the bars must be anchored for full strength on each side of the crack plane. For anchorage at a transverse boundary element, the bars may be grouted into the keyways or into slab cores where the top of the core is cut away. Concrete is then used to fill the cores for the length of the bar embedment. Based on a review of the literature, it is not clear when anchorage of collector bars in keyways is sufficient and when the collector bars should be placed in slab cores. There is a concern that as the boundary element and keyway crack, anchorage for a collector bar in a keyway may be lost. Deformations and reversible loading in a seismic event would suggest that anchoring collector bars in slab cores would be preferable in more intense seismic areas. In keeping with code philosophy, it is suggested that bars be anchored in slab cores in UBC zones 3 and 4

Fig. 4.9.1 Example Problem

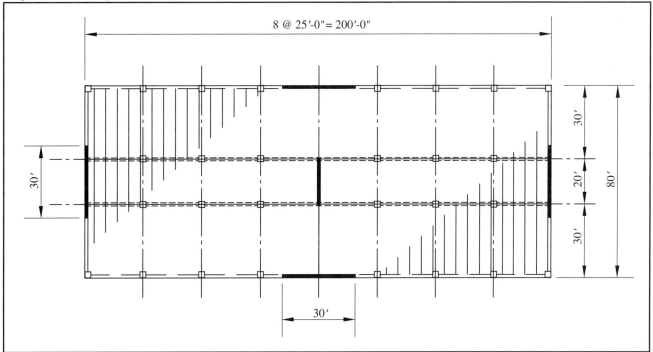

and BOCA Seismic Performance Categories C and greater.

In non-seismic and low seismic design situations, the collectors need not be reinforcing bars. Particularly for direct connections to lateral-resisting elements, welded and bolted connections will suffice for the collector connections when they are compatible with the slab system used.

4.8 Topped vs. Untopped Diaphragms

When a composite structural topping is provided, it should have a minimum thickness of 2 to 2 $\frac{1}{2}$ in (50-65 mm). The topping can then be designed as the diaphragm without consideration of the hollow core slabs. When the topping provides the strength and stiffness for the diaphragm but the connections are made in the hollow core slabs, shear stresses will be present at the interface of the topping and the hollow core slabs. These stresses will generally be well distributed throughout the interface, but may be more highly localized near the connections. As discussed in Chapter 2, horizontal shear stresses should be kept below a nominal strength of 80 psi (0.55 MPa).

The primary benefits of a composite structural topping are to increase stiffness and to allow easier continuous ties in plans with irregular shapes or large openings. However, in seismic areas, the additional topping weight increases the seismic

design forces. It is suggested that a topping be considered in high seismic zones in buildings with plan irregularities or large diaphragm span to depth ratios.

Untopped hollow core diaphragms are suggested when the diaphragm force system is straightforward and the in-plane diaphragm deflections are acceptable. An example at the end of this chapter illustrates a procedure for determining diaphragm deflections. In high seismic areas, local codes may limit the use of untopped, hollow core diaphragms.

4.9 Design Example

Given the building plan shown in Figure 4.9.1, design and detail the untopped hollow core diaphragm assuming:

   a. wind design per UBC
   b. Zone 2A seismic per UBC.

Building data
   6 stories
   14 ft floor to floor
   8 in hollow core floors wt = 53.5 psf
   partitions & mechanical wt = 20 psf
   precast framing system wt = 32 psf
   exterior wall system (avg.) wt = 35 psf

Solutions:

a. Seismic Zone 0; Basic wind speed 80 mph

Use Exposure C

Design wind pressure = $P = C_e C_q q_s I_w$

where

$C_e = 1.53$

$C_q = +0.8, -0.5$

$q_s = 16.4$

$I_w = 1.0$

$P = 1.53(0.8)(16.4)(1.0) = 20.1$

$\quad = 1.53(0.5)(16.4)(1.0) = \underline{12.5}$

$\qquad\qquad\qquad\qquad 32.6$ psf

Wind to diaphragm $= w = 14(0.0326) = 0.46$ k/ft

- Consider load applied parallel to the slabs

Total V = 200(0.46) = 92k

Assuming a rigid diaphragm, the shear distribution to the walls based on their flexural stiffness is:

30 ft walls: V = 40k

20 ft wall: V = 12k

The diaphragm equilibrium is:

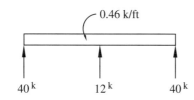

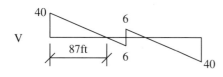

The factored design forces are then:

$V_{u30} = 1.3(40) = 52$k

$V_{u20} = 1.3(6) = 7.8$k

$M_u = 1.3(1739) = 2261$ ft-k

- Chord Forces:

Using the perimeter beams as chords:

$T_u = \dfrac{M_u}{\phi 0.8h}$

$\quad = \dfrac{2261}{0.9(0.8)(80)} = 39.3$k

Connect beams through columns for this force plus forces due to volume change and gravity loads. (Fig. 4.9.2 Det. C)

The chord must continue through the center wall.

$A_s = \dfrac{T_u}{f_y}$ (ϕ was included in T_u)

$\quad = \dfrac{39.3}{60}$

$\quad = 0.66$ in^2

Use 2 - #6 (Fig. 4.9.2 Det. F)

- Connect diaphragm web to chords

$V_{uh} = \dfrac{M_u}{jh}$

$j \cong 0.8$

$V_{uh} = \dfrac{2261}{0.8(80)}$

$\quad = 35.3$k

Distribute over length from zero moment to maximum moment

$V_{uh} = \dfrac{35.3}{87} = 0.41$k/ft

Additionally, this connection must resist the negative wind pressure from the exterior wall system.

$w_u = 1.3(0.0125)(14)$

$\quad = 0.23$k/ft

Use 300 lb/ft for structural integrity

(Fig. 4.9.2 Det. A)

The same forces must be resisted at the transverse joints. Use shear friction for the shear with bars placed in the keyways perpendicular to the transverse joint. With keyways at 3 ft on center:

$$A_s = \frac{3(0.3)}{0.9(60)} + \frac{3(0.41)}{0.85(60)(1.4)}$$

$$= 0.034 \text{ in}^2/\text{keyway}$$

Use #3 at every 2nd keyway

(Fig. 4.9.2 Det. B)

- Longitudinal shear

The maximum longitudinal joint shear is at the first slab joint from the 30 ft shear wall. Since connections will be made directly from the center bay to the shear wall, only the center bay joint length should be considered.

$$V_u = 52\text{k}$$

$$\phi V_n = \phi(0.08)h_n \ell$$

$$= 0.85(0.08)(8 - 2)(20 \times 12)$$

$$= 97.9\text{k}$$

With concerns for shrinkage cracking in joints, transverse shear friction reinforcement can be provided in the transverse joints at each end of the center bay.

$$A_{vf} = \frac{V_u}{\phi f_y \mu}$$

$$= \frac{52}{0.85(60)(1.0)}$$

$$= 1.02 \text{ in}^2 / 2 \text{ transverse joints}$$

$$= 0.51 \text{ in}^2 \text{ per joint}$$

Use 1 - #7 in transverse joint

(Fig. 4.9.2 Det. B)

- Shear connection to 30 ft wall

$$V_u = 52\text{k}$$

Additionally, negative wind pressure must be resisted across this joint, but would not be concurrent with shear. Structural integrity ties will control for this case.

$$T_u = (0.3)(20)$$

$$= 6\text{k for bay}$$

Using shear friction reinforcement

$$A_{vf} = 1.02 \text{ in}^2 \text{ (from above) or}$$

$$A_s = \frac{6}{0.9(60)} = 0.11 \text{ in}^2 \text{ does not control}$$

Use 4 - #5 located near slab ends

(Fig. 4.9.2 Det. D)

Alternatively, mechanical connections of slab to wall could be used to transfer the same forces.

- Shear at center 20 ft wall:

With the rigid diaphragm assumption:

$$V_u = 7.8\text{k on each side of wall}$$

$$A_{vf} = \frac{7.8}{0.85(60)(1.0)}$$

$$= 0.15 \text{ in}^2$$

Use 2 - #4 located near slab ends or use mechanical connections

(Fig. 4.9.2 Det. E)

- Consider load applied perpendicular to the slabs

Total V = 80(0.46) = 36.8k

Distribution to walls is:

$$V = 36.8/2$$

$$= 18.4\text{k}$$

The diaphragm equilibrium is:

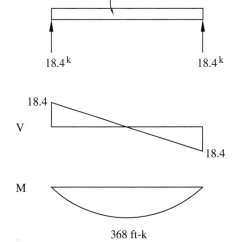

The factored design forces are then:

$$V_u = 1.3(18.4) = 23.9k$$

$$M_u = 1.3(368) = 478 \text{ ft-k}$$

- Chord force:

$$T_u = \frac{M_u}{\phi 0.8h}$$

$$= \frac{478}{0.9(0.8)(200)}$$

$$= 3.3k$$

$$A_s = \frac{3.3}{60} = 0.06 \text{ in}^2$$

The #3 bars across the transverse joints will be adequate for the chord force. (Fig. 4.9.2 Det. B)

Longitudinal shear

$$V_{uh} = \frac{M_u}{jh}$$

$$\cong \frac{478}{0.8(200)}$$

$$= 3.0k \text{ will not control}$$

- Shear connection to walls

Using shear friction reinforcement

$$V_u = 23.9k/30 \text{ ft wall}$$

$$= 0.8k/\text{ft controls over parallel wind}$$

With bars in keyways at 3 ft on center

$$A_{vf} = \frac{3(0.8)}{0.85(60)(1.4)}$$

$$= 0.034 \text{ in}^2 \text{ per keyway}$$

Use #3 in every 2nd keyway

(Fig. 4.9.2 Det. F)

- Shear in transverse joint

$$V_u = 1.3(18.4 - 0.46 \times 30)$$

$$= 6k$$

$$A_{vf} = \frac{6}{0.85(60)(1.0)}$$

$$= 0.12 \text{ in}^2$$

#3 at every 2nd keyway will be adequate

(Fig. 4.9.2 Det. B)

b. Seismic Zone 2A

The building weight attributable to each floor is:

$$w_i = 80(200)(0.0535 + 0.020 + 0.032)$$
$$+14(0.035)(200 + 80)(2)$$

$$= 1962k$$

then

$$W = 6(1962)$$

$$= 11772k$$

- Base shear

$$V = \frac{ZIC}{R_w}W$$

$$Z = 0.15$$

$$I = 1.0$$

$$C = 2.75$$

$$R_w = 8$$

$$V = \frac{0.15(1.0)(2.75)}{8}(11772)$$

$$= 607k$$

- Vertical Distribution

$$F_t = 0.07TV$$

with a site coefficient of 1.2 and C = 2.75

$$T = 0.4 \text{ sec} < 0.7 \text{ sec}$$

$$F_t = 0$$

$$F_x = \frac{(V - F_t)w_x h_x}{\sum\limits_{i=1}^{n} w_i h_i}$$

w_i	h_i	$w_x h_x$	F_x
1962	84	164808	173
1962	70	137340	145
1962	56	109872	116
1962	42	82404	87
1962	28	54936	58
1962	14	27468	29
		576828	

4–12

Fig. 4.9.2 Wind design summary

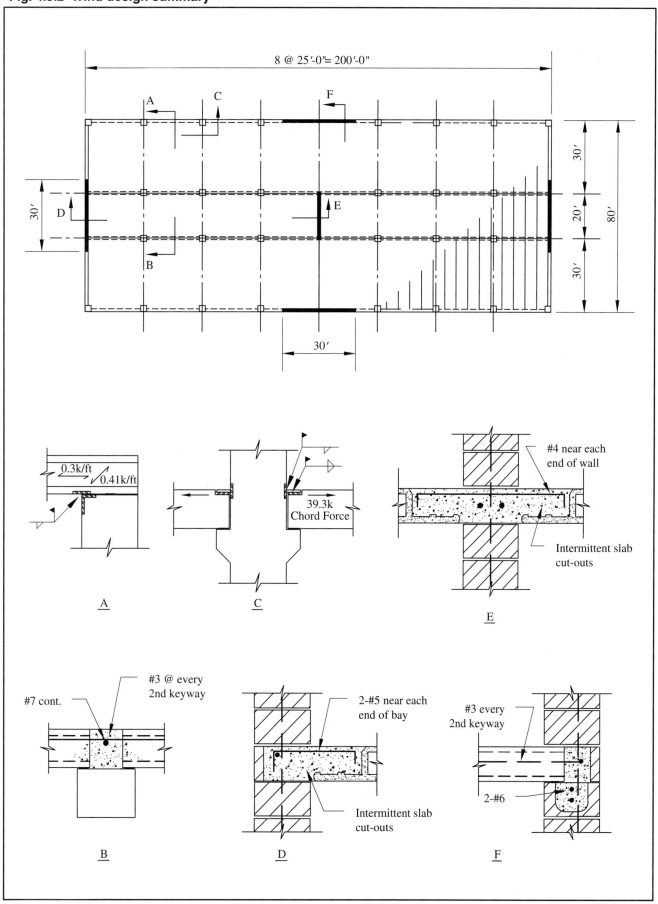

4–13

- Diaphragm load

$$F_{px} = \frac{F_t + \sum_{i=x}^{n} F_i}{\sum_{i=x}^{n} w_i} w_{px}$$

w_{px}	$F_t + \sum F_i$	$\sum w_i$	F_{px}
1962	173	1962	173
1962	318	3924	159
1962	434	5886	145
1962	521	7848	130
1962	579	9810	116
1962	607	11772	102

Minimum diaphragm load

$$F_{px} = 0.35ZIw_{px}$$

$$= 0.35(0.15)(1.0)(1962)$$

$$= 103k$$

Maximum diaphragm load

$$F_{px} = 0.75ZIw_{px}$$

$$= 0.75(0.15)(1.0)(1962)$$

$$= 221k$$

To keep diaphragm in the elastic range, multiply the diaphragm loads by 2R/5. At the roof

$$F_{pxu} = 173(2)(8)/5$$

$$= 554k$$

The factored roof diaphragm load by code provisions is

$$F_{pxu} = (1.1)(1.3)(173)$$

$$= 248k$$

Design roof diaphragm for a factored load of 554k to keep in elastic range.

- For shear parallel to slabs

Using a rigid diaphragm, the shear distribution to the walls is:

30 ft walls: $V = 241k$

20 ft wall: $V = 72k$

The diaphragm equilibrium is:

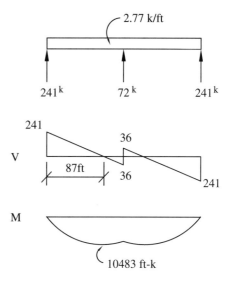

- Chord forces:

Using reinforcement in a perimeter boundary element

$$A_s = \frac{M_u}{\phi 0.8 h f_y}$$

$$= \frac{10483}{0.9(0.8)(80)(60)}$$

$$= 3.0 \text{ in}^2$$

Use 4 - #8

(Fig. 4.9.3 Det. A)

- Connect diaphragm web to chord

$$V_{uh} = \frac{M_u}{jd}$$

$$\cong \frac{10483}{0.8(80)}$$

$$= 164k$$

Distribute over length from zero moment to maximum moment

$$V_{uh} = \frac{164}{87} = 1.89k/ft$$

Additionally, this connection must resist the outward force from the exterior wall system. Conservatively, this force will be:

$$T = 0.75ZIw_w$$

$$= 0.75(0.15)(1.0)(14 \times 0.035)$$

$$= 0.055 \text{k/ft}$$

$$T_u = 0.055(2)(8)/5$$

$$= 0.176 \text{k/ft}$$

$$A_s = \frac{T_u}{\phi f_y} + \frac{V_u}{\phi f_y \mu}$$

$$= \frac{0.176}{0.9(60)} + \frac{1.89}{0.85(60)(1.4)}$$

$$= 0.033 \text{ in}^2/\text{ft}$$

Use #3 at 3 ft on center grouted into cores

(Fig. 4.9.3 Det. A)

At the transverse joint, the same shear parallel to the transverse joint as at the chord must be transferred. However, the tension should consider the inertial force from the weight of the exterior bay. Conservatively

$$T = 0.75 Z I w_p$$

$$w_p = 14(0.035) + 30(0.0535 + 0.020 + 0.032)$$

$$= 3.66 \text{k/ft}$$

$$T = 0.75(0.15)(1.0)(3.66)$$

$$= 0.41 \text{k/ft}$$

$$T_u = 0.41(2)(8)/5$$

$$= 1.31 \text{k/ft}$$

$$A_s = \frac{1.89}{0.85(60)(1.4))} + \frac{1.31}{0.9(60)}$$

$$= 0.051 \text{ in}^2/\text{ft}$$

Use #4 at 3 ft on center in keyways

(Fig. 4.9.3 Det. B)

- Longitudinal shear

The maximum longitudinal shear is at the first slab joint from the 30 ft wall. Provide shear friction reinforcement in the two transverse joints and the two boundary elements for shear resistance. Conservatively consider 5% minimum eccentricity being resisted only in end walls.

$$V_u = 241 + (0.05 \times 200)(554)/200$$

$$= 269 \text{k}$$

$$A_{vf} = \frac{269}{0.85(60)(1.0)}$$

$$= 5.27 \text{ in}^2 / 4 \text{ joints}$$

$$= 1.32 \text{ in}^2 \text{ per joint}$$

In boundary elements, add chord requirement

At first joint

$$M_u = 241(3) - 3^2(2.77)/2$$

$$= 711 \text{ ft-k}$$

$$A_s = 1.32 + \frac{711}{0.9(0.8)(80)(60)}$$

$$= 1.53 \text{ in}^2$$

4 - #8 ok

(Fig. 4.9.3 Det. A)

In transverse joints

$$A_s = 1.32 \text{ in}^2$$

Use 2 - #8

(Fig. 4.9.3 Det. B)

- Shear connection to 30 ft wall:

Transfer shear to wall and drag strut

$$V_u = \frac{253}{80}$$

$$= 3.16 \text{k/ft}$$

$$A_{vf} = \frac{3.16}{0.85(60)(1.0)}$$

$$= 0.062 \text{ in}^2/\text{ft}$$

Use #4 hairpins at 3 ft on center

(Fig. 4.9.3 Det. D)

Drag strut reinforcement

$$T_u = \frac{(80 - 30)}{2}(3.16)$$

$$= 79 \text{k}$$

$$A_s = \frac{79}{0.9(60)}$$

$$= 1.46 \text{ in}^2$$

Use 2 - #8

(Fig. 4.9.3 Det. C)

- Shear connection at 20 ft wall

    $V_u = 36k$

    over building width

    $V_u = \dfrac{36}{80} = 0.45k/ft$

    $A_{vf} = \dfrac{0.45}{0.85(60)(1.0)}$

    $= 0.009\ in^2/ft$

    Use #4 dowels at 8 ft on center

    (Fig. 4.9.3 Det. F)

    Drag strut reinforcement

    $T_u = \dfrac{(80-20)}{2}(0.45)(2)$

    $= 27k$

    $A_s = \dfrac{27}{0.9(60)}$

    $= 0.5\ in^2$

    Use 2 - #5

    (Fig. 4.9.3 Det. E)

- In-plane deflection of diaphragm

    Idealize the diaphragm section as

    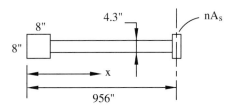

    with 4000 psi concrete in chord

    $E_c = 3835$

    with 5000 psi concrete in slab

    $E_c = 4300$

    normalize on slab concrete

    $n_{chord} = 0.89$

    $A_{Tchord} = 0.89(64)$

    $= 57\ in^2$

    $n_{steel} = 6.74$

$nA_s = 6.74(3.16)$

$= 21.3\ in^2$

$57(x-4) + 4.3(x-8)^2/2 = 21.3(956-x)$

find $x = 87.9$ in

$\begin{aligned}I_{cr} &= 57(87.9-4)^2 + 4.3(87.9-8)^3/3 \\ &\quad + 21.3(956-87.9)^2\end{aligned}$

$= 17,184,000\ in^4$

$= 829\ ft^4$

As a rigid diaphragm, the factored load deflection between end shear walls is:

$\Delta = \dfrac{5}{384}\dfrac{(2.77)(200)^4}{(4300)(829)(12)} - \dfrac{72(200)^3}{48(4300)(829)(12)}$

$= 1.07$ in (ignoring shear deflections)

As a flexible diaphragm with rigid supports the deflection will be substantially smaller. The diaphragm deflection plus the deflection of the lateral-resisting system is used to evaluate the gravity load support members for integrity when deformed.

- Consider load applied perpendicular to the slabs

Total $V_u = 554k$

Distribution to walls is

$V_u = 554/2$

$= 277k$

The diaphragm equilibrium is:

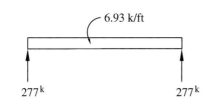

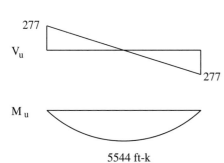

- Chord force

$$T_u = \frac{M_u}{\phi 0.8h}$$

$$= \frac{5544}{0.9(0.8)(200)}$$

$$= 38.5k$$

$$A_s = \frac{38.5}{60} = 0.64 \text{ in}^2$$

The #4 bars across the transverse joints at 3 ft on center will be adequate. (Fig. 4.9.3 Det. B)

Longitudinal shear

$$V_{uh} = \frac{M_u}{jd}$$

$$\cong \frac{5544}{0.80(200)}$$

$$= 34.7k \text{ will not control}$$

- Shear connection to walls

With 5% eccentricity

$$V_u = 1.1(277) = 304.7k$$

Transfer shear to wall and drag strut

$$V_u = 304.7/200 \text{ ft}$$

$$= 1.52k/\text{ft}$$

Loading parallel to slabs controls

Drag strut reinforcement

$$T_u = \frac{(200 - 30)}{2}(1.52)$$

$$= 129.2k$$

$$A_s = \frac{129.2}{0.9(60)} = 2.39 \text{ in}^2$$

Chord reinforcement from load parallel to slabs controls.

- Shear in transverse joint

In center bay

$$w_p = 20(200)(0.0535 + 0.020 + 0.032) + 20(14)(0.035)(2)$$

$$= 442k$$

Conservatively use

$$V = 0.75ZIw$$

$$= 0.75(0.15)(1.0)(442)$$

$$= 49.7k$$

$$V_u = 49.7(0.55)(2)(8)/5$$

$$= 87.5k \text{ per joint including } 5\% \text{ eccentricity}$$

Load parallel to slabs will control

See Figure 4.9.3 for summary

Fig. 4.9.3 Seismic design summary

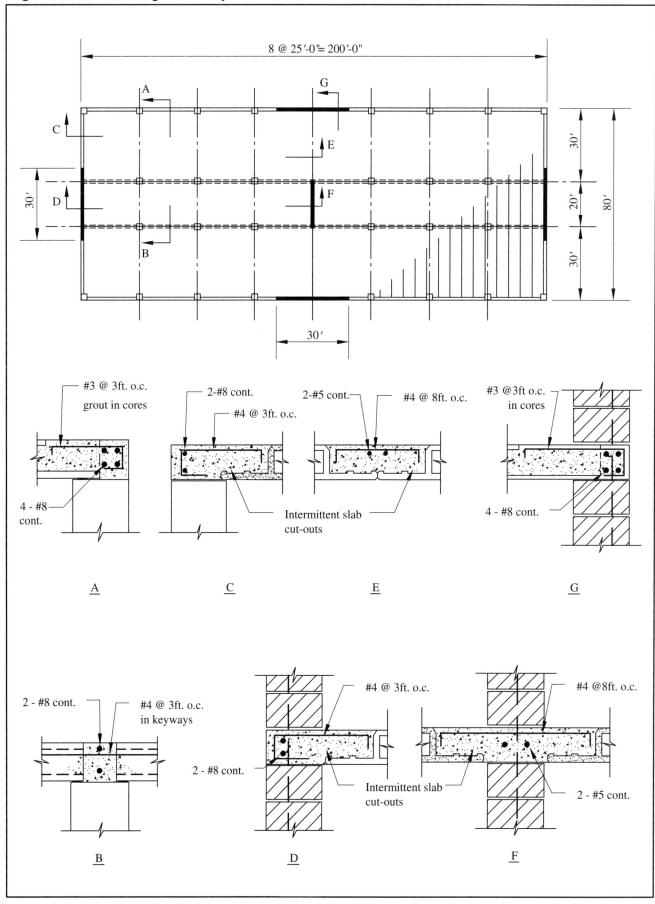

CHAPTER 5

CONNECTIONS IN HOLLOW CORE SLABS

5.1 General

Connections will be required in hollow core slab systems for a wide variety of reasons. Chapter 4 described the connection requirements for a hollow core diaphragm as an element for lateral stability. Most connection requirements will be for localized forces ranging from bracing a partition or beam to hanging a ceiling.

Connections are an expense to a project and, if used improperly, may have detrimental effects by not accommodating volume change movements that occur in a precast structure. Connections may develop forces as they restrain these movements. In specifying connection requirements, the actual forces in the connection must be addressed. If no force can be shown to exist, the connection should not be used. Again, cost is reduced and undesirable restraining forces will not be developed. When a connection is determined to be necessary, the force in the connection should be specified especially when at an interface between a hollow core slab and another material. The extent of detailing to be left to the hollow core slab supplier should be those items that will be supplied with the product.

5.2 Details

Common details are shown in Sections 5.3, 5.4, 5.5, and 5.6 to cover a number of conditions where forces will probably exist that need to be transmitted into or through a hollow core slab. The conditions cover common detailing situations when hollow core slabs are used and are intended to give the specifier an idea of the possibilities that exist. The commentary provided with each detail is intended to give a better understanding of the merits of each detail. The emphasis is that these provide a guide which can be used as a basis for better discussions with local producers. The details are only conceptual and would require detailed information to be used on a project.

Differences between wet cast and dry cast hollow core slabs will be evident in the embedded anchors that can be provided. Without forms to secure anchors to, dry cast systems may be limited to shallow anchors that can be tied directly to strands or to inserts that can be placed after casting. Wet cast systems can accommodate a wider variety of anchors placed directly in the form prior to casting. Therefore, anchor details in the hollow core slabs are not shown. Connection possibilities need to be explored with the local producers.

5.3 Typical Details with Concrete Beams

Design Considerations:

- Can transfer internal diaphragm forces
- Can be designed as structural integrity tie

Fabrication Considerations:

- Advantageous to have no hardware in slab
- Beam embedments must line up with slab joints
- Accommodates variations in slab length

Erection Considerations:

- Advantageous to have connection completed by follow-up crew
- Difficult for welder to hold loose plate in position

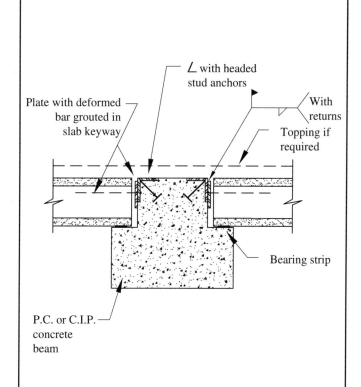

Fig. 5.3.1

Design Considerations:

- Can transfer internal diaphragm forces
- Can be designed as structural integrity tie

Fabrication Considerations:

- May increase beam reinforcement for shallower beam
- Layout must have opposing slab joints lined up

Erection Considerations:

- Clean and simple

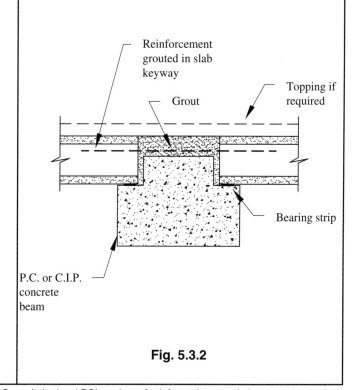

Fig. 5.3.2

Other connection details perform functions similar to those shown. Consult the local PCI producer for information on relative economy and design capabilities.

5.3 (Continued)

Design Considerations:

- With large factors of safety, friction may transfer nominal forces
- Additional structural integrity ties may be required

Fabrication Considerations:

- Clean and simple

Erection Considerations:

- Clean and simple

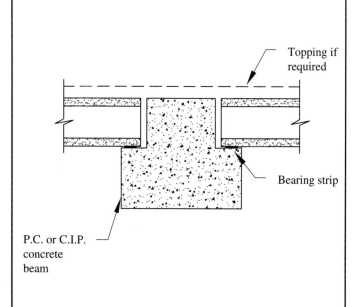

Topping if required

Bearing strip

P.C. or C.I.P. concrete beam

Fig. 5.3.3

Design Considerations:

- Can transfer internal diaphragm forces
- Can be designed as structural integrity tie
- Consider concrete cover on reinforcement over beam

Fabrication Considerations:

- Slab layout must have opposing joints lined up

Erection Considerations:

- Clean and simple

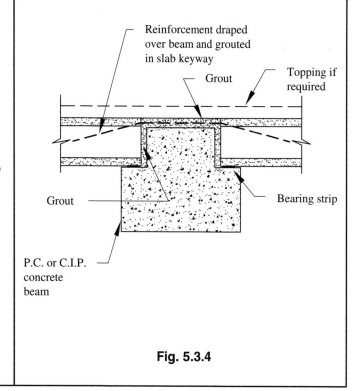

Reinforcement draped over beam and grouted in slab keyway

Grout

Topping if required

Grout

Bearing strip

P.C. or C.I.P. concrete beam

Fig. 5.3.4

Other connection details perform functions similar to those shown. Consult the local PCI producer for information on relative economy and design capabilities.

Design Considerations:

- Can transfer internal diaphragm forces
- Will develop volume change restraint forces that must be considered in design of connections

Fabrication Considerations:

- Slab manufacturing system must allow bottom weld anchors
- Beam inserts must align with slab inserts allowing fabrication tolerances

Erection Considerations:

- Connections can be completed by follow-up crew
- Access for welding may require ladders or scaffold
- Spacer may be required to make weld

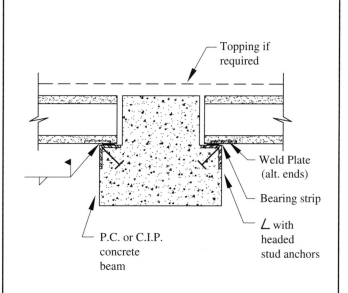

Fig. 5.3.5

Design Considerations:

- Can transfer internal diaphragm forces
- Can be designed as structural integrity tie
- Horizontal shear from beam cap must be transferred
- Opposing slab joints must line up

Fabrication Considerations:

- Clean and simple for slabs

Erection Considerations:

- Beam may have to be shored until cap is cured
- Horizontal shear reinforcement may present safety hazard for erector
- Core dams must be placed

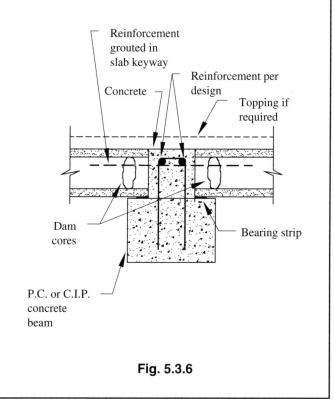

Fig. 5.3.6

Other connection details perform functions similar to those shown. Consult the local PCI producer for information on relative economy and design capabilities.

Design Considerations:

- Can transfer internal diaphragm forces
- Can be designed as structural integrity tie
- Horizontal shear in composite beam must be transferred
- Opposing slab joints must line up

Fabrication Considerations:

- Clean and simple for slabs

Erection Considerations:

- Beam may have to be shored until topping is cured
- Horizontal shear reinforcement may present safety hazard for erector
- Core dams must be placed

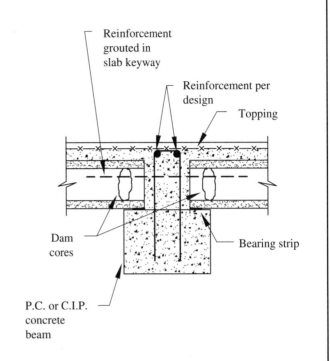

Fig. 5.3.7

Design Considerations:

- Can transfer diaphragm shear
- Can provide lateral brace for beam
- Potential for negative moment in slabs

Fabrication Considerations:

- Slab insert difficult to install. Because of tolerance on sawcut ends, the insert should be installed after slabs are cut to length
- Beam and slab inserts must align

Erection Considerations:

- If required for lateral beam stability, welding may have to be completed as slabs are set

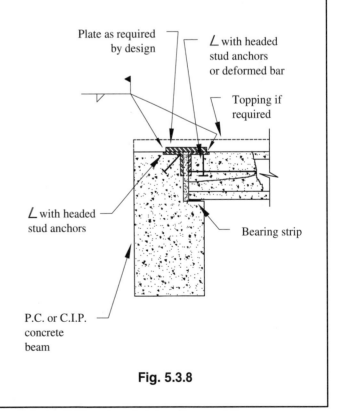

Fig. 5.3.8

Other connection details perform functions similar to those shown. Consult the local PCI producer for information on relative economy and design capabilities.

Design Considerations:

- Can transfer diaphragm shear
- Can provide lateral brace for beam
- Potential to develop negative moment in slabs

Fabrication Considerations:

- Plates in beam must align with slab joints allowing tolerance

Erection Considerations:

- Connection can be completed with a follow-up crew
- Lateral bracing for beam will not be provided until keyway grout cures

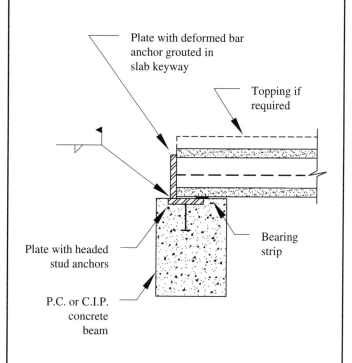

Fig. 5.3.9

Design Considerations:

- Can transfer internal diaphragm forces
- Can be designed as structural integrity tie

Fabrication Considerations:

- Clean and simple

Erection Considerations:

- Clean and simple
- Keyway dimensions may limit the reinforcement diameter

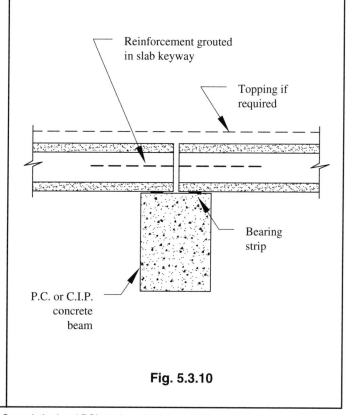

Fig. 5.3.10

Other connection details perform functions similar to those shown. Consult the local PCI producer for information on relative economy and design capabilities.

5.3 (Continued)

Design Considerations:

- Can transfer diaphragm shear
- Can be designed as structural integrity tie

Fabrication Considerations:

- Clean and simple for both beam and slabs

Erection Considerations:

- Reinforcement must be tied in place
- Concrete must be cast around reinforcement
- Edge form is required for cast-in-place concrete
- Dowels from beam may present safety hazard

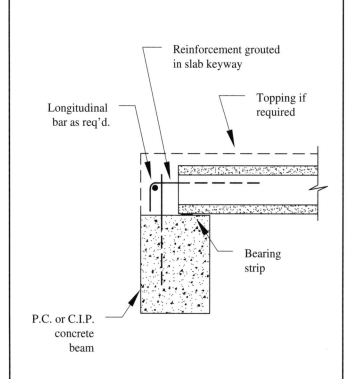

Fig. 5.3.11

Design Considerations:

- Can transfer internal diaphragm forces
- Will develop volume change restraint forces that must be considered in design of connection

Fabrication Considerations:

- Slab manufacturing system must allow bottom weld inserts
- Beam and slab inserts must align with allowance for tolerance

Erection Considerations:

- Connections can be completed by follow-up crew
- Access for welding may require ladders or scaffold
- Spacer may be required to make weld

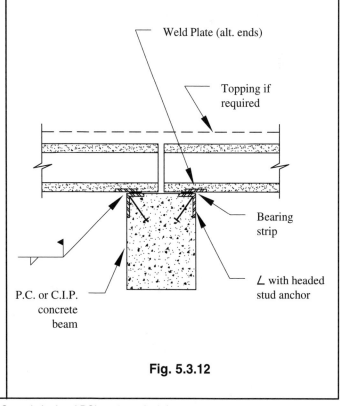

Fig. 5.3.12

Other connection details perform functions similar to those shown. Consult the local PCI producer for information on relative economy and design capabilities.

Design Considerations:

- Can transfer diaphragm shear
- Torsional and lateral beam restraint can be provided
- Will develop volume change restraint forces that must be considered in design of connection

Fabrication Considerations:

- Slab manufacturing system must allow bottom weld inserts
- Beam and slab weld anchors must align with allowances for tolerance

Erection Considerations:

- Connections can be completed by follow-up crew
- Access for welding may require ladders or scaffold
- Spacer may be required to make weld

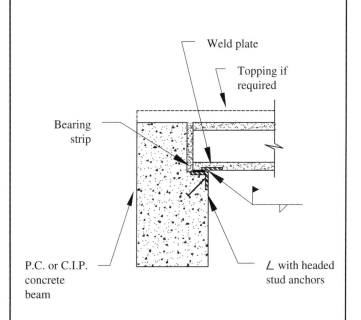

Fig. 5.3.13

Design Considerations:

- This detail is not recommended because of installation difficulties which may result in an unreliable connection

Fabrication Considerations:

- Great difficulty aligning bars with keyways

Erection Considerations:

- Potential difficulties in bending bars
- Possible fracture of bent bars
- Second rebar bend may be required to align with slab joints
- Cast-in-place concrete required around reinforcement
- Edge forming required

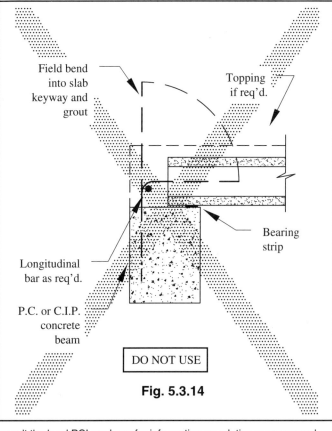

DO NOT USE

Fig. 5.3.14

Other connection details perform functions similar to those shown. Consult the local PCI producer for information on relative economy and design capabilities.

5.4 Typical Details with Walls

Design Considerations:

- Can transfer diaphragm shear
- Can be designed as structural integrity tie
- Can provide lateral brace for wall
- Consider axial force path through slab ends
- Opposing slab joints must line up

Fabrication Considerations:

- Clean and simple for slabs
- Small tolerance for placement of bars in walls
- Tolerance on length of slabs to accommodate bars in joint

Erection Considerations:

- With longitudinal bar, have potential congestion
- Slab erection must consider tight tolerance on butt joint gap
- With precast walls, consider method of installing vertical dowel

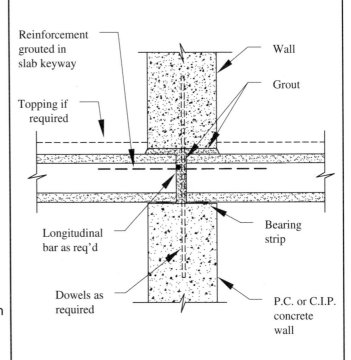

Fig. 5.4.1

Design Considerations:

- Can transfer diaphragm shear
- Can be designed as structural integrity tie
- Can provide lateral brace for wall
- Opposing slab joints must line up

Fabrication Considerations:

- Clean and simple for slabs

Erection Considerations:

- Clean and simple
- Wall is not braced until grout is placed and cured

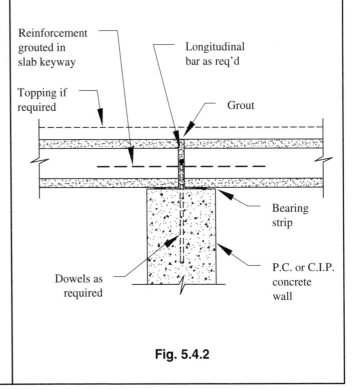

Fig. 5.4.2

Other connection details perform functions similar to those shown. Consult the local PCI producer for information on relative economy and design capabilities.

5.4 (Continued)

Design Considerations:

- Can transfer diaphragm shear
- Can provide lateral brace for wall with proper bar detailing
- Consideration should be given to forces developed as slab ends rotate

Fabrication Considerations:

- Clean and simple

Erection Considerations:

- Simple for slab erection
- The mason can set bars independent of the slab joints
- Some block cutting may be required for bars from keyways

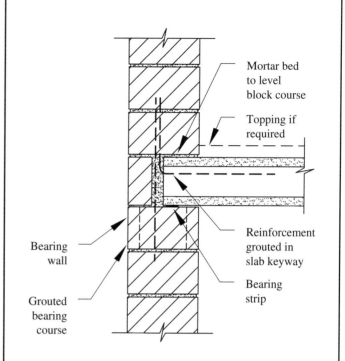

Fig. 5.4.3

Mortar bed to level block course

Topping if required

Reinforcement grouted in slab keyway

Bearing strip

Bearing wall

Grouted bearing course

Design Considerations:

- Can transfer diaphragm shear
- Can provide lateral brace for wall with proper detailing
- Consideration should be given to forces developed as slab ends rotate

Fabrication Considerations:

- Clean and simple

Erection Considerations:

- Simple for slab erection
- The mason can set bars independent of the slab joints
- Grout at slab end may be difficult to place

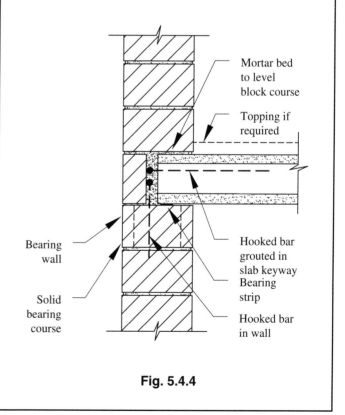

Fig. 5.4.4

Mortar bed to level block course

Topping if required

Hooked bar grouted in slab keyway

Bearing strip

Hooked bar in wall

Bearing wall

Solid bearing course

Other connection details perform functions similar to those shown. Consult the local PCI producer for information on relative economy and design capabilities.

Design Considerations:

- This detail is not recommended because of installation difficulties which may result in an unreliable connection

Fabrication Considerations:

Erection Considerations:

- Mason will have great difficulty locating bars at slab joints
- Potential difficulties to field bend bars including fracture
- Second bend may be required to align bars with joints

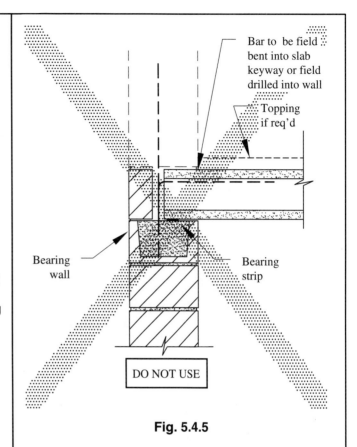

Fig. 5.4.5

Design Considerations:

- Wall will not be braced at this level

Fabrication Considerations:

- Clean and simple

Erection Considerations:

- Small tolerance in slab layout

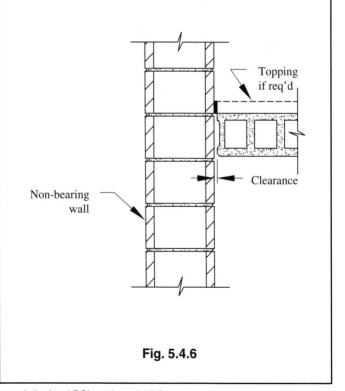

Fig. 5.4.6

Other connection details perform functions similar to those shown. Consult the local PCI producer for information on relative economy and design capabilities.

5.4 (Continued)

Design Considerations:

- Walls may not be laterally braced
- Consideration should be given to forces developed from deflections or camber growth
- Drypack may be required under slab for axial load transfer

Fabrication Considerations:

- Clean and simple

Erection Considerations:

- Allowance must be made for slab camber
- Wall will not be laterally braced at this level
- Small tolerance in slab layout

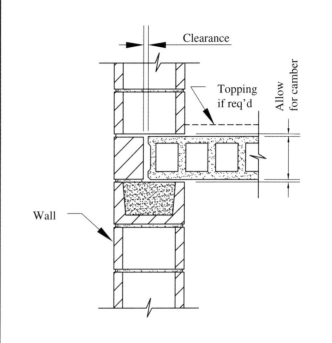

Fig. 5.4.7

Design Considerations:

- Can transfer diaphragm shear
- Can provide lateral brace for wall
- Consideration should be given to forces developed from deflection or camber growth
- Consider axial load path

Fabrication Considerations:

- If not done in field, slots and holes must be cut for steel
- In stack casting system slots and holes might not be practically cut in plant

Erection Considerations:

- Allowance must be made for slab camber
- If not done in plant, holes and slots must be cut for steel
- Wall is not braced until steel is grouted

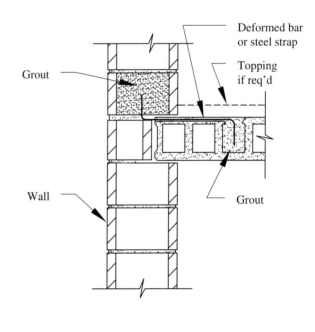

Fig. 5.4.8

Other connection details perform functions similar to those shown. Consult the local PCI producer for information on relative economy and design capabilities.

5.4   (Continued)

Design Considerations:

- Wall thrust from earth pressure can be resisted
- Can transfer diaphragm shear only with special detailing of keyway and reinforcement
- For long spans consider effects of restraint of vertical movement

Fabrication Considerations:

- Clean and simple

Erection Considerations:

- Edge joint must be grouted which may not be standard practice

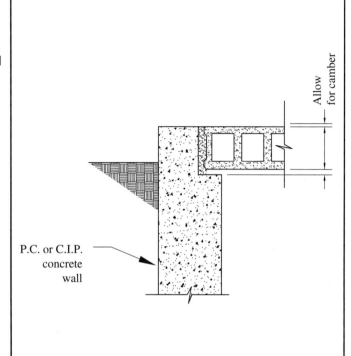

Fig. 5.4.9

Design Considerations:

- Can transfer diaphragm shear
- Can provide lateral brace for wall
- Consideration should be given to forces developed from deflections or camber growth

Fabrication Considerations:

- If not done in field, edge core must be cut open
- In stack casting operation, holes might not be practically cut in plant

Erection Considerations:

- If not done in plant, holes must be field cut into edge core
- Mason may have to cut block to install reinforcement

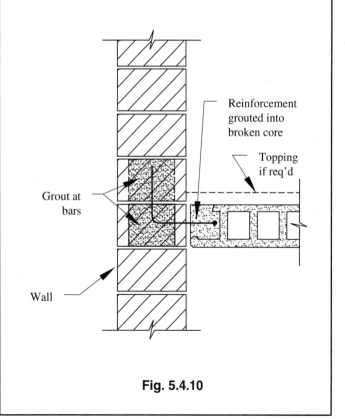

Fig. 5.4.10

Other connection details perform functions similar to those shown. Consult the local PCI producer for information on relative economy and design capabilities.

5.4 (Continued)

Design Considerations:

- Can transfer diaphragm shear
- Can provide lateral brace for wall
- Connection capacity must be verified by test

Fabrication Considerations:

- Clean and simple

Erection Considerations:

- Minimum edge distances must be maintained
- No interfacing tolerances

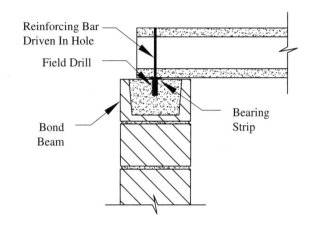

Fig. 5.4.11

Design Considerations:

- Can transfer diaphragm shear
- Can provide lateral brace for wall
- Consider effects of vertical restraint
- Connection capacity must be verified by test

Fabrication Considerations:

- Clean and simple

Erection Considerations:

- Minimum edge distances must be maintained
- No interfacing tolerances

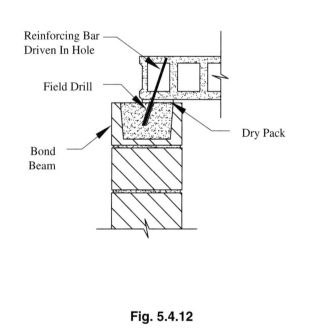

Fig. 5.4.12

Other connection details perform functions similar to those shown. Consult the local PCI producer for information on relative economy and design capabilities.

5.5 Typical Details with Steel Beams

Design Considerations:

- Top beam flange should be considered unbraced

Fabrication Considerations:

- Clean and simple for slabs
- Beam flange width must be sufficient for slab bearing length

Erection Considerations:

- Unsymmetrical loading may cause beam instability

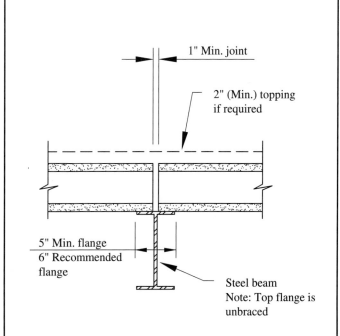

1" Min. joint

2" (Min.) topping if required

5" Min. flange
6" Recommended flange

Steel beam
Note: Top flange is unbraced

Fig. 5.5.1

Design Considerations:

- Can transfer internal diaphragm forces
- Provides lateral brace for steel beam

Fabrication Considerations:

- Slab layout must align slab joints
- Stabilizer bars might be field or shop installed depending on local regulations or agreements
- Beam flange width must be sufficient for minimum slab bearing

Erection Considerations:

- Grouting of slabs must include the butt joint
- Steel erection may require that stabilizer bars be field installed
- Steel beam will not be laterally braced until grout cures
- Unsymmetrical loading may cause beam instability

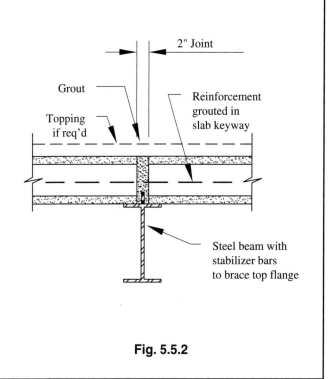

2" Joint

Grout

Topping if req'd

Reinforcement grouted in slab keyway

Steel beam with stabilizer bars to brace top flange

Fig. 5.5.2

Many connection details shown perform similar functions. Consult the local PCI producer for information on relative economy and design capabilities.

Design Considerations:

- Can transfer internal diaphragm forces
- Provides lateral brace for steel beam
- Will develop volume change restraint forces that must be considered in design of connection

Fabrication Considerations:

- Slab manufacturing system must allow for installation of bottom weld anchors

Erection Considerations:

- Welding of slabs to beam should be done as erection proceeds to laterally brace beams

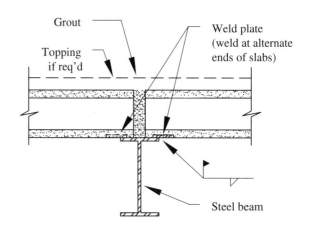

Fig. 5.5.3

Design Considerations:

- Can transfer diaphragm shear
- Provides lateral brace for steel beam
- Potential torsion on steel beam should be considered
- Will develop volume change restraint forces that must be considered in design of connection

Fabrication Considerations:

- Slab manufacturing system must allow for installation of bottom weld anchors

Erection Considerations:

- Welding of slabs to beam should be done as erection proceeds to brace beam
- Spacer may be required to make weld

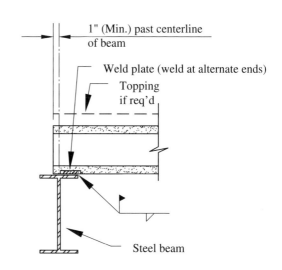

Fig. 5.5.4

Other connection details perform functions similar to those shown. Consult the local PCI producer for information on relative economy and design capabilities.

Design Considerations:

- Can transfer diaphragm shear
- Provides lateral brace for steel beam

Fabrication Considerations:

- Clean and simple

Erection Considerations:

- Welding of bars must be coordinated with slab erection for alignment
- Depending on forces to be transferred concrete may have to be cast along edge
- Beam will not be braced until keyway grout cures

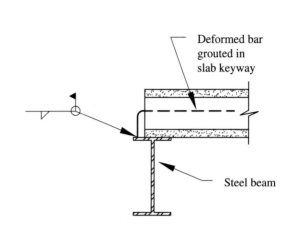

Fig. 5.5.5

Design Considerations:

- Internal diaphragm forces can be transferred only through topping
- Provides lateral brace for steel beam
- Consider potential torsion on beam during slab erection

Fabrication Considerations:

- Beam flange width must be sufficient for minimum slab bearing
- Slab notching will require a hand operation in field or, preferably, in plant

Erection Considerations:

- Slab erection will be very difficult with this detail on both slab ends. Slabs must be slid into beams possibly through access holes in flanges
- Beams will not be braced during slab erection

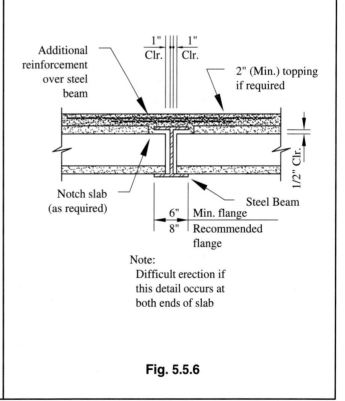

Fig. 5.5.6

Other connection details perform functions similar to those shown. Consult the local PCI producer for information on relative economy and design capabilities.

Design Considerations:

- Internal diaphragm forces can be transferred only through topping
- Provides lateral brace for steel beam
- Consider potential torsion in beam during slab erection

Fabrication Considerations:

- Angle legs must be sufficient for minimum slab bearing
- Beam depth must be sufficient for clearance under top flange

Erection Considerations:

- Slab erection will be very difficult if this detail occurs at both slab ends. Slabs will have to be slid into beams possibly through access holes in flanges
- Beams will not be braced during slab erection

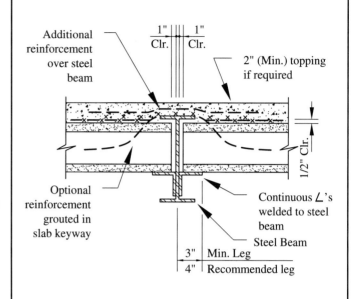

Note:
Difficult erection if this detail occurs at both ends of slab

Fig. 5.5.7

Design Considerations:

- Torsion design must consider erection tolerance
- Lintel must be securely anchored at span ends
- Connection to slab may be required to brace lintel

Fabrication Considerations:

- Clean and simple

Erection Considerations:

- Watch for stability of lintel prior to slab erection

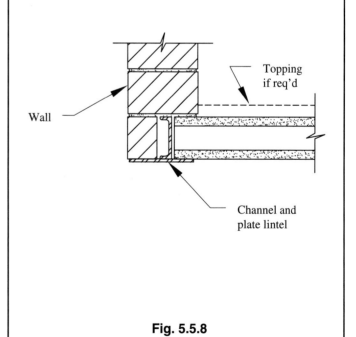

Fig. 5.5.8

Other connection details perform functions similar to those shown. Consult the local PCI producer for information on relative economy and design capabilities.

Design Considerations:

- Butt joint must be grouted to brace vertical angle legs
- Lintel must be securely anchored at span ends

Fabrication Considerations:

- Clean and simple

Erection Considerations:

- Lintel must be securely anchored prior to setting slabs

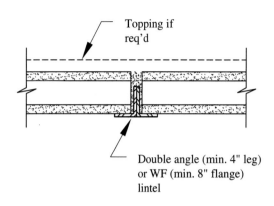

Topping if req'd

Double angle (min. 4" leg) or WF (min. 8" flange) lintel

Fig. 5.5.9

Design Considerations:

- Clearance must be allowed for slab camber
- Beam will not be braced until topping is cast

Fabrication Considerations:

- Camber must be monitored to stay within clearance

Erection Considerations:

- Erection may be very difficult if slab support beams are also raised

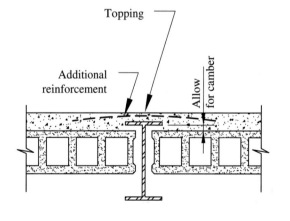

Topping

Additional reinforcement

Allow for camber

Fig. 5.5.10

Other connection details perform functions similar to those shown. Consult the local PCI producer for information on relative economy and design capabilities.

5.6 Typical Cantilever Details

Design Considerations:

- Wall bracing or transmitting diaphragm shear would only be accomplished by questionable friction
- Additional structural integrity ties may be required

Fabrication Considerations:

- None other than top reinforcement required for cantilever

Erection Considerations:

- Clean and simple

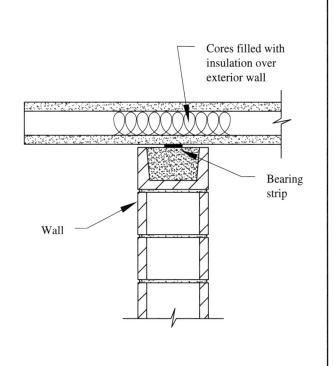

Fig. 5.6.1

Design Considerations:

- Can transfer diaphragm shear
- Provides lateral brace for wall

Fabrication Considerations:

- If not field drilled, slots in keyways and aligning holes in masonry are required
- If not field drilled, alignment will be difficult

Erection Considerations:

- If not preformed, holes must be drilled through slabs into masonry
- Wall may not be braced until grout cures
- Grout placement may be difficult

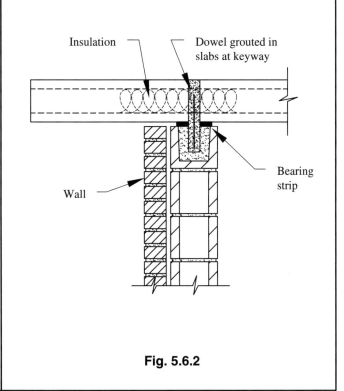

Fig. 5.6.2

Other connection details perform functions similar to those shown. Consult the local PCI producer for information on relative economy and design capabilities.

5.6 (Continued)

Design Considerations:

- This detail is not recommended because of installation difficulties which may result in an unreliable connection

Fabrication Considerations:

Erection Considerations:

- Mason will have great difficulty aligning dowels with slab joints
- Most keyway configurations will require notches for dowels
- Field bending of dowels into keyways will be very difficult

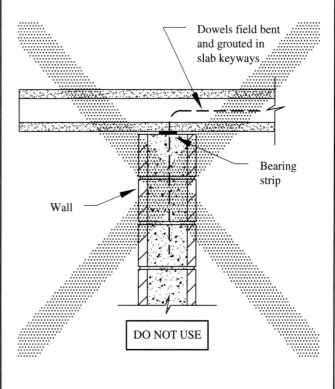

Fig. 5.6.3

Design Considerations:

- Wall will not be braced by slabs
- Depending on end support conditions wall may have to support edge slab
- No thermal break provided between interior and exterior

Fabrication Considerations:

- Depending on bearing conditions the overhang dimension may be limited by the producer's ability to install transverse reinforcement

Erection Considerations:

- None

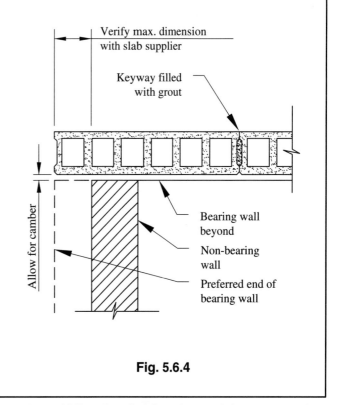

Fig. 5.6.4

Other connection details perform functions similar to those shown. Consult the local PCI producer for information on relative economy and design capabilities.

5.6 (Continued)

Design Considerations:

- Wall will not be braced by slabs
- Depending on end support conditions wall may have to support edge slab
- No thermal break provided between interior and exterior

Fabrication Considerations:

- When transverse reinforcement cannot be installed, steel strap must serve as external reinforcement
- Anchorage of a steel strap to the slabs will depend on the producer's ability to install top weld anchors

Erection Considerations:

- Depending on end support conditions temporary shoring may be required until steel strap is installed and keyways are grouted

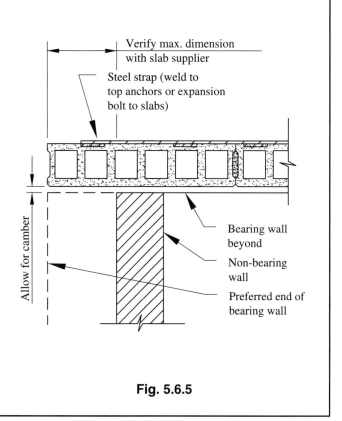

Fig. 5.6.5

Other connection details perform functions similar to those shown. Consult the local PCI producer for information on relative economy and design capabilities.

5.7 Miscellaneous Details

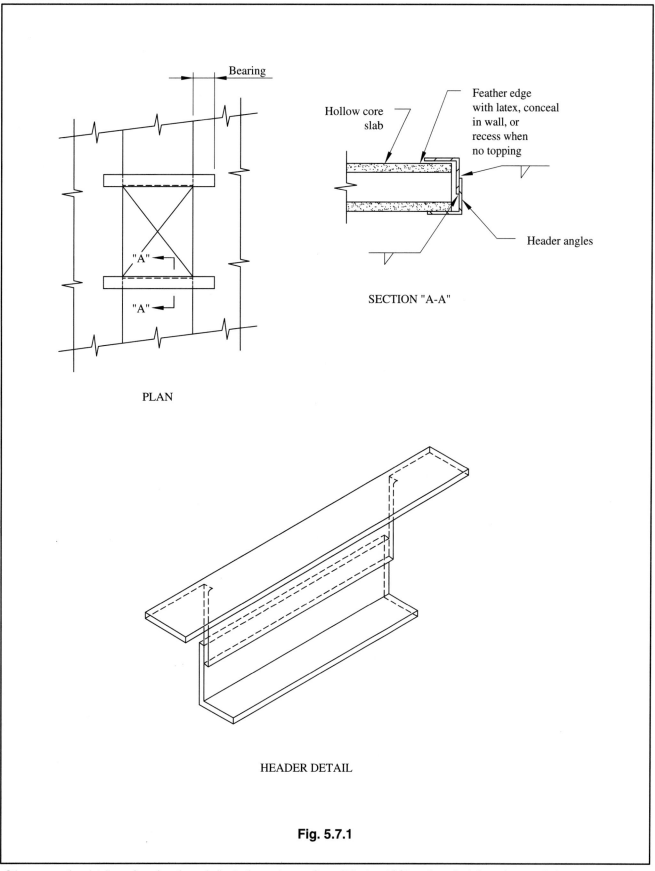

Bearing

Hollow core
slab

Feather edge
with latex, conceal
in wall, or
recess when
no topping

Header angles

"A"

"A"

SECTION "A-A"

PLAN

HEADER DETAIL

Fig. 5.7.1

Other connection details perform functions similar to those shown. Consult the local PCI producer for information on relative economy and design capabilities.

5.7 (Continued)

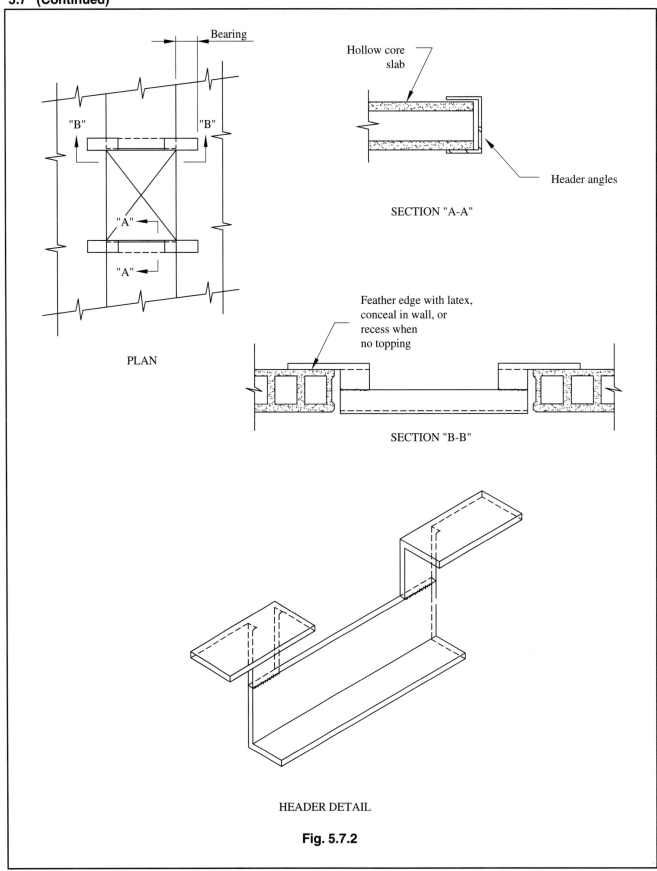

Bearing

"B" "B"

"A"

"A"

PLAN

Hollow core slab

Header angles

SECTION "A-A"

Feather edge with latex, conceal in wall, or recess when no topping

SECTION "B-B"

HEADER DETAIL

Fig. 5.7.2

Other connection details perform functions similar to those shown. Consult the local PCI producer for information on relative economy and design capabilities.

5.7 (Continued)

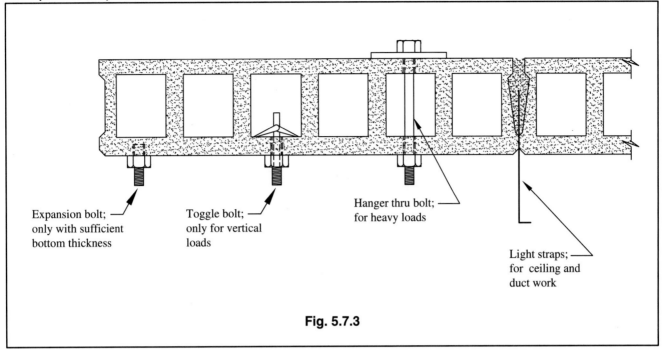

Expansion bolt; —
only with sufficient
bottom thickness

Toggle bolt; —
only for vertical
loads

Hanger thru bolt; —
for heavy loads

Light straps; —
for ceiling and
duct work

Fig. 5.7.3

Other connection details perform functions similar to those shown. Consult the local PCI producer for information on relative economy and design capabilities.

CHAPTER 6

FIRE RESISTANCE OF ASSEMBLIES
MADE WITH HOLLOW CORE SLABS

6.1 Introduction

One of the attributes of hollow core slab construction is excellent fire resistance. More than 30 standard fire tests (ASTM E119) have been conducted on hollow core floor assemblies. The January, 1994 issue of Underwriters Laboratories, Inc. "Fire Resistance Directory" includes more than 50 design numbers for hollow core slabs which qualify for ratings of 1, 2, 3, or 4 hours. Constructions which conform to these designs are assigned ratings by most U.S. building codes.

As an alternative to UL ratings, model codes now include prescriptive requirements which can be used to establish fire endurance ratings. For each fire endurance rating, strand cover and equivalent thickness provisions are given. Use of such provisions eliminates the need for fire tests or UL ratings.

Most U.S. building codes will also assign ratings to hollow core assemblies which do not conform with the UL designs if it can be shown by calculations made in accordance with procedures given in the PCI manual, "Design for Fire Resistance of Precast, Prestressed Concrete" (PCI MNL 124-89)[38] that they qualify for the required fire endurance. Readers can obtain more detailed information from that manual on fire resistance of hollow core slab assemblies as well as information on fire resistance of concrete beams, walls, and protection of connections.

In Canada, The National Building Code of Canada requires that fire resistance ratings be determined either on the basis of results of tests conducted in accordance with CAN/ULC-S101-M, "Standard Methods of Fire Endurance Tests of Building Construction and Materials", or on the basis of Appendix D, "Fire Performance Ratings". While the general principles set forth in this Manual are fully valid in that they are based on materials properties and structural engineering procedures, users of the Manual are cautioned that in Canada, fire resistance ratings should be determined strictly in accordance with applicable building code requirements.

6.2 Heat Transmission Through Floors or Roofs

The standard fire test method, ASTM E119, limits the average temperature rise of the unexposed surface, i.e., the surface of floor or roof not exposed to fire, to 250 degrees F (120 degrees C) during a fire test. This criterion is often called the heat transmission end point.

For solid concrete slabs, the temperature rise of the unexposed surfaces depends mainly on the slab thickness and aggregate type. Figure 6.2 shows the relationship between slab thickness and fire endurance as determined by the heat transmission end point criterion.

6.2.1 Equivalent Thickness

The information in Figure 6.2 is applicable to hollow core slabs by entering the graph with the "equivalent thickness" of the unit instead of the thickness. Equivalent thickness can be calculated by dividing the net area of the cross section of a hollow core unit by the width of the unit.

Fig. 6.2   Fire endurance (heat transmission) of hollow core units

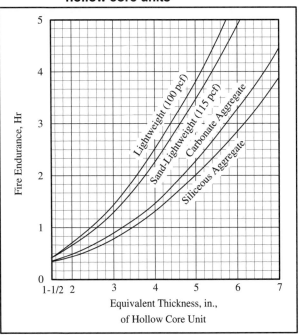

In Figure 6.2, concrete aggregates are designated as lightweight, sand-lightweight, carbonate, or siliceous. Lightweight aggregates include expanded clay, shale, slate, and slag which produce concretes having unit weights between about 95 and 105 pcf (1520 - 1680 kg/m³) without sand replacement. Lightweight concretes in which sand is used as part or all of the fine aggregate and weigh less than about 120 pcf (1920 kg/m³) are designated as sand-lightweight. For normal weight concrete, the type of coarse aggregate influences the fire endurance; the type of fine aggregate has only a minor effect. Carbonate aggregates include limestone, dolomite, and limerock, i.e., those consisting mainly of calcium or magnesium carbonate. Siliceous aggregates include quartzite, granite, basalt, and most hard rocks other than limestone or dolomite.

6.2.2 Toppings, Undercoatings, or Roof Insulation

All 8 in (200 mm) deep hollow core units which are currently manufactured in North America qualify for at least a one-hour fire endurance as determined by heat transmission and some qualify

for two hours or more. The addition of toppings, undercoatings, fire resistive ceilings, roof insulation, or filling the cores with dry aggregates will increase the heat transmission fire endurance. Figure 6.2.2.1 shows graphically the thickness of spray applied undercoating required for heat transmission fire endurances of 2, 3 and 4 hours. Figure 6.2.2.2 shows the thickness of sand-lightweight concrete, insulating concrete and high strength gypsum concrete overlays required for 2, 3 and 4 hours. Figure 6.2.2.3 shows data for 2 and 3 hr. roofs with mineral board or glass fiber board insulation with 3-ply built-up roofing. Data shown in Figures 6.2.2.1, 6.2.2.2 and 6.2.2.3 apply directly to hollow core slabs made with siliceous aggregates and are conservative for slabs made with carbonate aggregates or with lightweight aggregates.

Example 6.2.1 Equivalent Thickness
Determine the thickness of topping required to provide a 3 hr. fire endurance (heat transmission) for the generic hollow core slab shown in Figure 1.7.1. Both the slab and the topping are made with carbonate aggregate concrete.

Fig. 6.2.2.1 Hollow core units undercoated with spray applied materials (Heat transmission fire endurance)

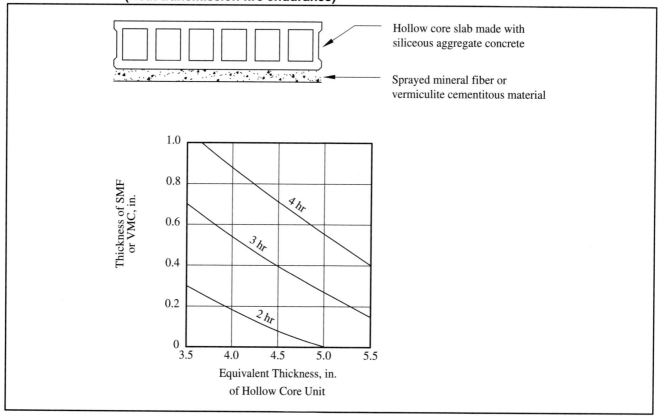

Fig. 6.2.2.2 Floors with overlays of sand-lightweight concrete (120 pcf maximum), insulating concrete (35 pcf maximum), and high strength gypsum concrete

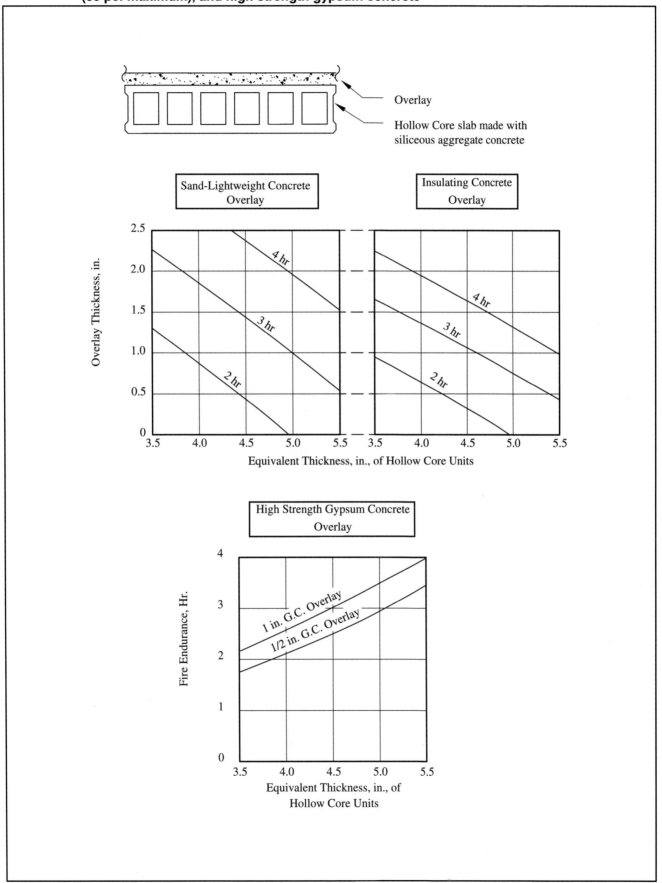

**Fig. 6.2.2.3   Roofs with insulation board and 3-ply built-up roofing
(Heat transmission fire endurance)**

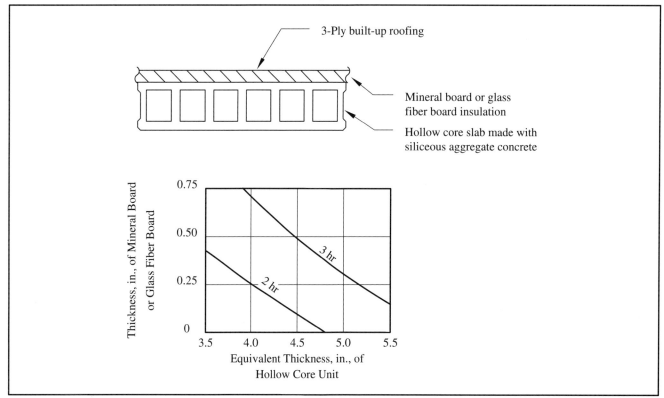

Solution:

Equivalent thickness

t_{eq} =   Area/width

=   154/36

=   4.28 in

From Figure 6.2, the thickness of carbonate aggregate concrete required for 3 hr. is 5.75 in. Thus, the thickness of topping needed is:

$$5.75 - 4.28 = 1.47 \text{ in}$$

Example 6.2.2

Determine if a hollow core slab roof will qualify for a 2 hr. fire endurance (heat transmission) if the slabs are made with carbonate aggregate concrete, have an equivalent thickness of 4.28 in, and the roof insulation consists of a layer of $^3/_4$ in thick mineral board. The roofing is a standard 3-ply built-up roof.

Solution:

From Figure 6.2.2.3 it can be seen that with an equivalent thickness of 4.28 in, a layer of mineral board 0.16 in thick with 3-ply roofing qualifies for 2 hours even if the slabs are made with siliceous aggregates. With carbonate aggregate concrete, the required thickness would be even less. Thus, the roof qualifies for a fire endurance significantly longer than 2 hours.

6.2.3 Ceilings

Gypsum wallboard used as ceilings increases the fire endurance of the assemblies. Very few fire tests have been conducted utilizing concrete floors with gypsum wallboard ceilings, and no such tests have been conducted utilizing hollow core units. To be effective, gypsum wallboard must remain in place throughout most of the fire endurance period. Because most hollow core units by themselves have heat transmission fire endurances of one hour to two hours and longer, the wallboard must remain in place during fire exposure for long periods of time. For a fire endurance of 3 hours, a layer of $^5/_8$ in (16 mm) Type X gypsum wallboard can be used. The wallboard should be installed as shown in Figure 6.2.3.

6.3 Structural Fire Endurance of Floor or Roof Assemblies

During standard fire tests, specimens must support the anticipated superimposed loads through-

Fig. 6.2.3 Details of 3 hr. assembly consisting of hollow core slabs with a gypsum wall board ceiling

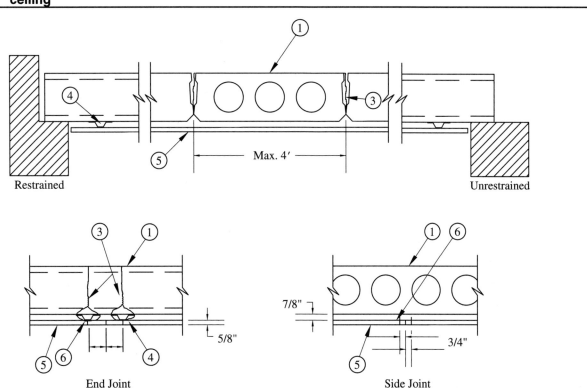

Restrained   Unrestrained

End Joint   Side Joint

1. <u>Precast concrete hollow core slabs</u> – Minimum equivalent thickness = 2.75 in

2. <u>Grout</u> – (Not Shown) – Sand–cement grout along full length of joint.

3. <u>Hanger Wire</u> – No. 18 SWG galvanized steel wire. Hanger wire used to attached wallboard furring channels to precast concrete units. Wire to be located at each intersection of furring channels and joints between hollow core slabs, but not to exceed 4 ft o.c.

4. <u>Wallboard Furring Channels</u> – No. 26 ga. galvanized steel, $7/8$ in high, $2\ 3/4$ in base width, $1\ 3/8$ in face width and 12 ft long. Channels to be installed perpendicular to hollow core slabs and spaced 24 in o.c., except at wallboard butt joints where they are spaced $6\ 1/2$ in o.c. Channels secured to concrete units with double strand of hanger wire looped through fasteners. At furring channel splices, channels to be overlapped 6 in and tied together with hanger wire at each end of splice.

5. <u>Wallboard</u> – $5/8$ in thick, 4 ft wide, Type X, installed with long dimension perpendicular to furring channels. Over butt joints, a 3 in wide piece of wallboard to be inserted with ends extending a minimum 6 in beyond board width.

6. <u>Wallboard Fasteners</u> – 1 in long, Type S, bugle head screws. Fasteners spaced 12 in on center along each furring channel except at butt joints where fasteners spaced 8 in on center. At butt joints, fasteners located $3\ 1/4$ in from board edge. Along side joints, fasteners located $3/4$ in from board edge.

7. <u>Joint System</u> – (Not Shown) – Paper tape embedded in cementitious compound over joints, and covered with two layers of cementitious compound with edges feathered out. Wallboard fastener heads covered with two layers of cementitious compound.

out the fire endurance period. Failure to support the loads is called the structural end point.

The most important factor affecting the structural fire endurance of a floor or roof assembly is the method of support, i.e., whether the assembly is simply supported and free to expand ("unrestrained") or if the assembly is continuous or thermal expansion is restricted ("restrained").

6.3.1 Simply Supported Slabs

Figure 6.3.1.1 illustrates the behavior of a simply supported slab exposed to fire from beneath. Because strands are parallel to the axis of the slab,

the ultimate moment capacity is constant throughout the length:

$$\phi M_n = \phi A_{ps} f_{ps}(d_p - a/2) \qquad \text{(Eq. 6.3.1)}$$

See Chapter 2 for evaluating f_{ps}.

If the slab is uniformly loaded, the moment diagram will be parabolic with a maximum value at midspan of:

$$M = \frac{w\ell^2}{8} \qquad \text{(Eq. 6.3.2)}$$

**Fig. 6.3.1.1 Moment diagrams for simply sup-
ported beam or slab before and
during fire exposure**

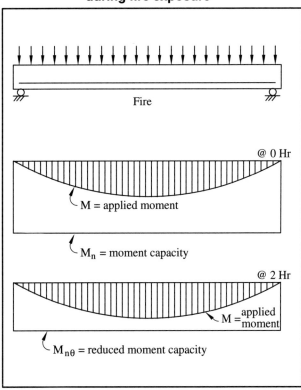

Where

w = dead plus live load per unit of length,
k/in

ℓ = span length, in

As the material strengths diminish with elevated temperatures, the retained moment capacity
becomes:

$$M_{n\theta} = A_{ps}f_{ps\theta}(d_p - a_\theta /2) \qquad \text{(Eq. 6.3.3)}$$

in which θ signifies the effects of high temperatures. Note that A_{ps} and d_p are not affected, but f_{ps}
is reduced. Similarly, a is reduced, but the concrete strength at the top of the slab, f'_c, is generally
not reduced significantly because of its lower
temperature.

Fig. 6.3.1.2 Temperature-strength relationships for hot-rolled and cold-drawn steels

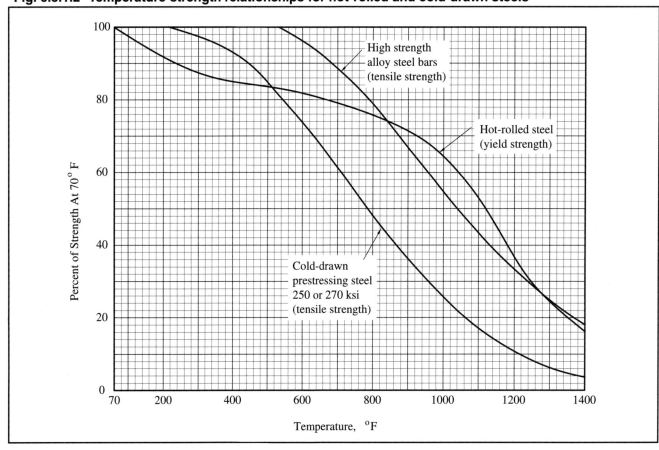

Fig. 6.3.1.3 Temperatures within carbonate aggregate concrete slabs during fire tests

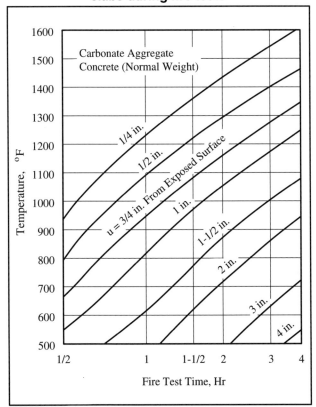

Fig. 6.3.1.4 Temperatures within siliceous aggregate concrete slabs during fire tests

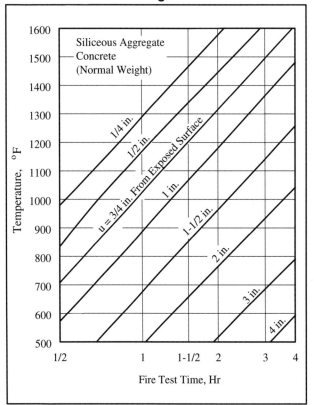

Flexural failure can be assumed to occur when $M_{n\theta}$ is reduced to M. From this expression, it can be seen that the fire endurance depends on the applied loading and on the strength-temperature characteristics of the steel. In turn, the duration of the fire before the "critical" steel temperature is reached depends upon the protection afforded to the reinforcement.

Test results have shown that the theory discussed above is valid, not only for hollow core floors, but also for roofs with insulation on top of the slabs.

Figure 6.3.1.2 shows the relationship between temperature and strength of various types of steel. Figure 6.3.1.3, 6.3.1.4 and 6.3.1.5 show temperatures within concrete slabs during standard fire tests. The data in those figures are applicable to hollow core slabs. By using the equations given above and the data in Figure 6.3.1.2 through 6.3.1.5, the moment capacity of slabs can be calculated for various fire endurance periods, as illustrated in the following example:

Fig. 6.3.1.5 Temperatures within sand-lightweight concrete slabs during fire tests

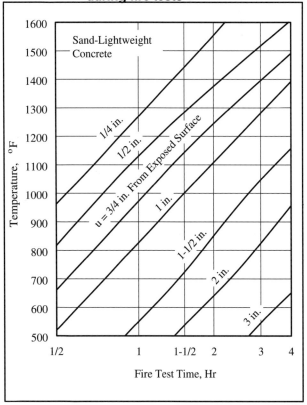

Example 6.3.1

Determine the maximum safe superimposed load that can be supported by an 8 in deep hollow core slab with a simply supported unrestrained span of 25 ft and a fire endurance of 3 hr.

Given:

$h = 8$ in; $u = 1.75$ in; six $^1/_2$ in 270 ksi strands; $A_{ps} = 6(0.153) = 0.918$ in^2; $b = 36$ in; $d_p = 8 - 1.75 = 6.25$ in; $w_D = 54$ psf; carbonate aggregate concrete; $\ell = 25$ ft

Solution:

(a) Estimate strand temperature at 3 hr. from Figure 6.3.1.3, θ_s at 3 hr. at 1.75 in above fire-exposed surface = 925 degrees F.

(b) Determine $f_{pu\theta}$ from Figure 6.3.1.2. For cold-drawn steel at 925 degrees F:

$f_{pu\theta} = 33\%\ f_{pu} = 89.1$ ksi

(c) Determine $M_{n\theta}$ and w

$$f_{ps\theta} = 89.1 \left[1 - \frac{0.28}{0.80} \left(\frac{0.918}{36(6.25)} \frac{89.1}{5} \right) \right]$$

$= 86.8$ ksi

$$a_\theta = \frac{0.918(86.8)}{0.85(5)(36)} = 0.52\,\text{in}$$

$M_{n\theta} = 0.918(86.8)(6.25 - 0.52/2)/12$

$= 39.8$ ft-kips

$$w = \frac{8(39.8)(1000)}{(25)^2(3)} = 170\ \text{psf}$$

$w_L = w - w_D = 170 - 54 = 116$ psf

(d) Calculate maximum allowable w_L at room temperature

$$f_{ps} = 270 \left[1 - \frac{0.28}{0.80} \left(\frac{0.918}{36(6.25)} \frac{270}{5} \right) \right]$$

$= 249$ ksi

$$a = \frac{0.918(249)}{0.85(5)(36)} = 1.49\ \text{in}$$

$\phi M_n = 0.9(0.918)(249)(6.25 - 0.75)/12$

$= 94.3$ ft-kips

$$w_u = \frac{8(94.3)(1000)}{(25)^2(3)} = 402\ \text{psf}$$

With load factors of 1.4 (dead load) + 1.7 (live load):

$$w_L = \frac{402 - 1.4(54)}{1.7} = 192\ \text{psf}$$

Conclusion: $w_L = 116 < 192$; 116 psf governs

Note: Fire endurance for heat transmission should also be checked

Table 6.3.1 shows values of u for simply supported unrestrained hollow core slabs for various moment ratios and fire endurance of 1, 2, and 3 hours. The values shown are based on $A_{ps}f_{pu}/bd_pf'_c = 0.05$ and can be reduced by $^1/_{16}$ in for $A_{ps}f_{pu}/bd_pf'_c = 0.10$.

Table 6.3.1 "u" inches, for simply supported unrestrained hollow core slabs*

Fire Endurance (hr)	M/M$_n$	Aggregate Type					
		Siliceous (in)	(mm)	Carbonate (in)	(mm)	Sand-Lightweight (in)	(mm)
1	0.50	$1\,^1/_4$	(32)	$1\,^1/_{16}$	(27)	$1\,^1/_{16}$	(27)
1	0.40	$1\,^1/_{16}$	(27)	$^{15}/_{16}$	(24)	$^{15}/_{16}$	(24)
1	0.30	$^{15}/_{16}$	(24)	$^{13}/_{16}$	(21)	$^{13}/_{16}$	(21)
2	0.50	$1\,^{15}/_{16}$	(49)	$1\,^{13}/_{16}$	(46)	$1\,^{13}/_{16}$	(46)
2	0.40	$1\,^3/_4$	(44)	$1\,^9/_{16}$	(40)	$1\,^9/_{16}$	(40)
2	0.30	$1\,^9/_{16}$	(40)	$1\,^5/_{16}$	(33)	$1\,^5/_{16}$	(33)
3	0.50	$2\,^1/_2$	(64)	$2\,^5/_{16}$	(59)	$2\,^1/_8$	(54)
3	0.40	$2\,^3/_{16}$	(56)	2	(51)	$1\,^{15}/_{16}$	(49)
3	0.30	$1\,^{15}/_{16}$	(49)	$1\,^{11}/_{16}$	(43)	$1\,^{11}/_{16}$	(43)

*"u" is distance between center of strands and bottom of slab with all strands having same "u". Based on $A_{ps}f_{pu}/bd_pf'_c = 0.05$; conservative for values greater than 0.05.

Fig. 6.3.2 Equivalent concrete cover thickness for spray-applied coatings

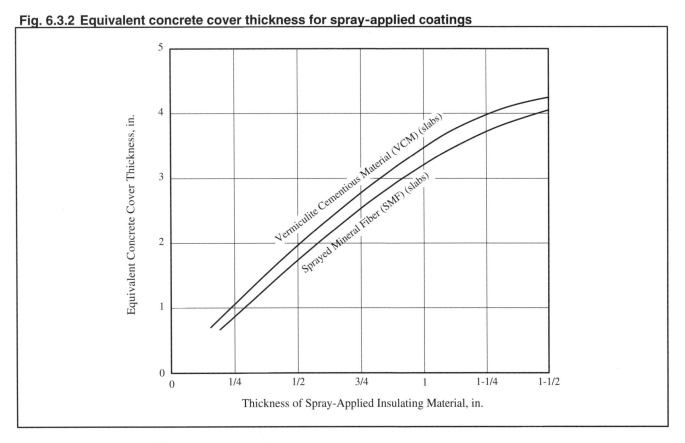

6.3.2 Effect of Spray-Applied Coatings

The fire endurance of hollow core slabs can be increased by the addition of a spray-applied coating of vermiculite cementitious material or sprayed mineral fiber. Figure 6.3.2 shows the relationship between thickness of spray-applied coatings and equivalent concrete cover. Thus, if strands are centered $^3/_4$ in (19 mm) above the bottom of a hollow core slab and if $^1/_4$ in (6 mm) of sprayed mineral fiber is applied, the u distance to be used in Figures 6.3.1.3, 6.3.1.4 or 6.3.1.5 is $^3/_4$ in (19 mm) plus the equivalent cover of 0.9 in (23 mm) obtained from Figure 6.3.2.

6.3.3 Structurally Continuous Slabs

Continuous members undergo changes in stresses when subjected to fire, resulting from temperature gradients within the structural members, or changes in strength of the materials at high temperatures, or both.

Figure 6.3.3.1 shows a continuous beam whose underside is exposed to fire. The bottom of the beam becomes hotter than the top and tends to expand more than the top. This differential temperature causes the ends of the beam to tend to lift from their supports thereby increasing the reaction at

Fig. 6.3.3.1 Moment diagrams for continuous 2-span beam before and during fire exposure

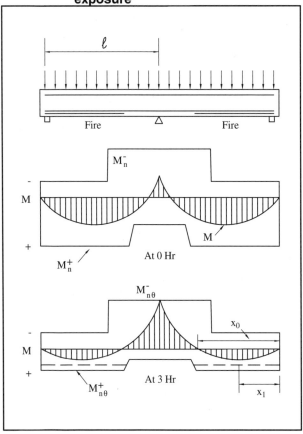

Fig. 6.3.3.2 Uniformly loaded member continuous at one support

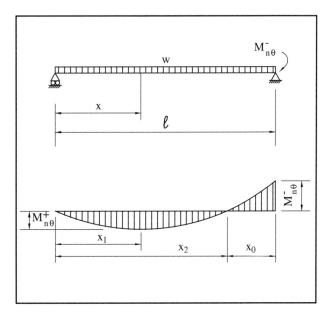

Fig. 6.3.3.3 Symmetrical uniformly loaded member continuous at both supports

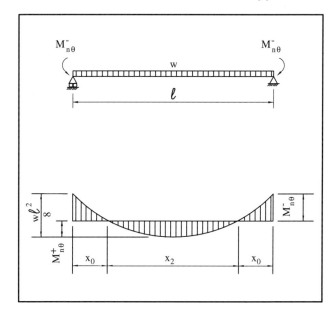

the interior support. This action results in a redistribution of moments, i.e., the negative moment at the interior support increases while the positive moments decrease.

During the course of a fire, the negative moment reinforcement (Figure 6.3.3.1) remains cooler than the positive moment reinforcement because it is better protected from the fire. Thus, the increase in negative moment can be accommodated. Generally, the redistribution that occurs is sufficient to cause yielding of the negative moment reinforcement. The resulting decrease in positive moment means that the positive moment reinforcement can be heated to a higher temperature before a failure will occur. Therefore, the fire endurance of a continuous concrete beam is generally significantly longer than that of a simply supported beam having the same cover and loaded to the same moment intensity.

It is possible to design the reinforcement in a continuous beam or slab for a particular fire endurance period. From Figure 6.3.3.1, the beam can be expected to collapse when the positive moment capacity, $M_{n\theta}^+$, is reduced to the value indicated by the dashed horizontal line, i.e., when the redistributed moment at point x_1, from the outer support, $M_{x_1} = M_{n\theta}^+$.

Figure 6.3.3.2 shows a uniformly loaded beam or slab continuous (or fixed) at one support and

simply supported at the other. Also shown is the redistributed applied moment diagram at failure.

Values for $M_{n\theta}^+$ can be calculated by the procedures given for "Simply Supported Slabs".

Values for $M_{n\theta}^-$ and x_0 can be calculated:

$$M_{n\theta}^- = \frac{w\ell^2}{2} \pm w\ell^2 \sqrt{\frac{2M_n^+}{w\ell^2}} \qquad \text{(Eq. 6.3.4)}$$

$$x_0 = 2\frac{M_{n\theta}^-}{w\ell} \qquad \text{(Eq. 6.3.5)}$$

In most cases, redistribution of moments occurs early during the course of a fire before the negative moment capacity has been reduced by the effects of fire. In such cases, the length of x_0 is increased, i.e., the inflection point moves toward the simple support. For such cases,

$$x_0 = \frac{2M_n^-}{w\ell} \qquad \text{(Eq. 6.3.6)}$$

Figure 6.3.3.3 shows a symmetrical beam or slab in which the end moments are equal. In that case:

$$M_{n\theta}^- = w\ell^2/8 - M_{n\theta}^+ \qquad \text{(Eq. 6.3.7)}$$

and $\dfrac{wx_2^2}{8} = M_{n\theta}^+ \qquad \text{(Eq. 6.3.8)}$

In negative moment regions, the compressive zone is directly exposed to fire, so calculations for d_θ^- and a_θ^- must be modified by (a) using $f_{c\theta}'$ from Figure 6.3.3.4 and (b) neglecting concrete hotter than 1400 degrees F (760 degrees C).

Fig. 6.3.3.4 Compressive strength of concrete at high temperatures

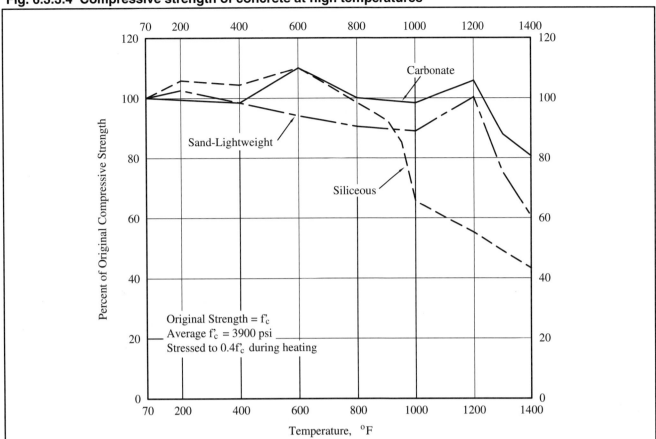

6.3.4 Detailing Precautions

It should be noted that the amount of moment redistribution that can occur is dependent upon the amount of negative reinforcement. Tests have clearly demonstrated that the negative moment reinforcement will yield, so the negative moment capacity is reached early during a fire test, regardless of the applied loading. The designer must exercise care to ensure that a secondary type of failure will not occur. To avoid a compression failure in the negative moment region, the amount of negative moment reinforcement should be small enough so that ω_θ, i.e., $A_s f_{y\theta}/b_\theta d_\theta f'_{c\theta}$, is less than 0.30, before and after reductions in f_y, b, d and f'_c are taken into account. Furthermore, the negative moment bars or mesh must be long enough to accommodate the complete redistributed moment and change in the inflection points. It should be noted that the worst condition occurs when the applied loading is smallest, such as dead load plus partial or no live load. It is recommended that at least 20% of the maximum negative moment reinforcement be extended throughout the span.

Example 6.3.2

Determine the amount of negative moment reinforcement needed to provide a 3 hr. fire endurance for sand-lightweight hollow core slabs, 8 in deep, 5 ksi concrete, 48 in wide, with six $7/16$ in 270 ksi strands and 2 in (4 ksi) composite topping. Slabs span 25 ft of an exterior bay (no restraint to thermal expansion). Dead load = 65 psf, live load = 100 psf. Strands are centered $1\,3/4$ in above bottom of slab. The value for $M_{n\theta}^+$ can be calculated (by using the procedure discussed for simply supported slabs) to be 39.0 ft-kips. From Eq. 6.3.4 (for use in Eq. 6.3.4):

$$w\ell^2 = 4(65 + 100)(25)^2/1000$$
$$= 412.5 \text{ ft-kips}$$

$$M_{n\theta}^- = \frac{412.5}{2} - 412.5\sqrt{2\frac{(39.0)}{412.5}}$$
$$= 26.9 \text{ ft-kips}$$

Determine A_s^- neglecting concrete above 1400 degrees F in negative moment region. From Figure 6.3.1.5 neglect $3/4$ in above bottom, and assume steel centered in topping.

$$d = 10 - 3/4 - 1 = 8.25 \text{ in}$$

Assume $f'_{c\theta}$ in compressive zone $= 0.8f'_c = 4$ ksi
Assume $\bar{d} - \bar{a}_\theta/2 = 8.1$ in

$$\bar{A}_s = \frac{26.9(12)}{60(8.1)} = 0.66 \text{ in}^2$$

check $\bar{a}_\theta = \dfrac{0.66(60)}{0.85(4)48} = 0.24$ in

$\bar{d} - \bar{a}_\theta/2 = 8.25 - 0.12 = 8.13$ in $\cong 8.1$ OK

Use 6 x 6 - W2.1 x W2.1 WWF throughout plus #4 Grade 60 at 16 in in negative moment region.

$$\bar{A}_s = 8(0.021) + \frac{48}{16}(0.20) = 0.768 \text{ in}^2$$

Calculate x_o for dead load plus one-half live load.

$$\bar{M}_{n\theta} = \frac{0.768}{0.66}(26.9) = 31.3 \text{ ft-kips}$$

loading $= 4(0.065 + 0.050) = 0.46$ k/ft;

$\bar{M}_n = 34.0$ ft-kips (calculated for room temperatures)

From Eq. 6.3.6

$$x_o = \frac{2\bar{M}_n}{w\ell} = \frac{2(34.0)}{0.46(25)} = 5.91 \text{ ft}$$

Half of #4 bars should extend 7 ft each side of interior support and half 5 ft.
Use #4 Grade 60, 12 ft long at 16 in and stagger.

6.4 Restraint to Thermal Expansion

If a fire occurs beneath a portion of a large floor or roof, such as beneath a concrete floor slab in one interior bay of a multi-bay building, the heated portion will expand and push against the surrounding unheated portion. In turn the unheated portion exerts compressive forces on the heated portion. The compressive force, or thrust, acts near the bottom of the slab when the fire starts, but as the fire progresses, the line of thrust rises and the thermal gradient diminishes and the heated concrete undergoes a reduction in elastic modulus. If the surrounding slab is thick and heavily reinforced, the thrust forces can be quite large, but they will be considerably less than those calculated by use of elastic properties of concrete and steel, together with appropriate coefficients of expansion. At high temperatures, creep and stress relaxation play an important role. Nevertheless, the thrust is generally great enough to increase the fire endurance significantly, in some instances by more than 2 hours. In most fire tests of restrained assemblies, the fire endurance is determined by

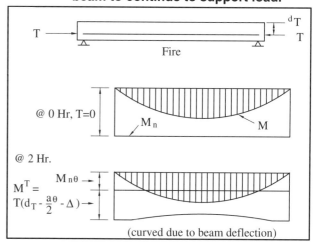

Fig. 6.4.1 Moment diagrams for axially restrained beam during fire exposure. Note that at 2 hr. $M_{n\theta}$ is less than M and effects of axial restraint permit beam to continue to support load.

temperature rise of the unexposed surface rather than by structural considerations, even though the steel temperatures often exceed 1200 degrees F (650 degrees C).

The effects of restraint to thermal expansion can be characterized as shown in Figure 6.4.1. The thermal thrust, T, acts in a manner similar to an external prestressing force, which tends to increase the positive moment capacity.

Methods for calculating fire endurance of "restrained" floors or roofs are given in PCI MNL 124-89. It is seldom necessary to make such calculations, as noted below. The beneficial effects of restraint are recognized in ASTM E119. The standard presents a guide for determining conditions of restraint. The guide includes Figure 6.4.2. In most cases, the interior bays of multi-bay floors and roofs can be considered to be restrained and the magnitude and location of the thrust are generally of academic interest only. It should be noted that Figure 6.4.2 indicates that adequate restraint can occur in interior bays and exterior bays of framed buildings when:

"The space between the ends of precast units and the vertical faces of supports, or between the ends of solid or hollow core slab units does not exceed 0.25 percent of the length for normal weight concrete members or 0.1 percent of the length for structural lightweight concrete members".

Sketches illustrating typical conditions described above are shown in Figure 6.4.3.

Fig. 6.4.2. Examples of typical restrained and unrestrained construction classifications (from Appendix X3 of ASTM E119-88)

I. Wall Bearing:
Single span and simply supported end spans of multiple bays[a]
(1)	Open-web steel joists or steel beams, supporting concrete slab, precast units or metal decking	unrestrained
(2)	Concrete slabs, precast units or metal decking	unrestrained

Interior spans of multiple bays:
(1)	Open-web steel joists, steel beams or metal decking, supporting continuous concrete slab	restrained
(2)	Open-web steel joists or steel beams, supporting precast units or metal decking	unrestrained
(3)	Cast-in-place concrete slab systems	restrained
(4)	Precast concrete where the potential thermal expansion is resisted by adjacent construction[b]	restrained

II. Steel Framing:
(1)	Steel beams welded, riveted, or bolted to the framing members	restrained
(2)	All types of cast-in-place floor and roof systems (such as beam-and-slabs, flat slabs, pan joints, and waffle slabs) where the floor or roof system is secured to the framing members	restrained
(3)	All types of prefabricated floor or roof systems where the structural members are secured to the framing members and the potential thermal expansion of the floor or roof system is resisted by the framing system or the adjoining floor or roof construction[b]	restrained

III. Concrete Framing:
(1)	Beams securely fastened to the framing members	restrained
(2)	All types of cast-in-place floor or roof systems (such as beam-and-slabs, flat slabs, pan joists, and waffle slabs) where the floor system is cast with framing members	restrained
(3)	Interior and exterior spans of precast systems with cast-in-place joints resulting in restraint equivalent to that which would exist in condition III(1)	restrained
(4)	All types of prefabricated floor or roof systems where the structural members are secured to such systems and the potential thermal expansion of the floor or roof system is resisted by the framing system or the adjoining floor or roof construction[b]	restrained

IV. Wood Construction
All Types	unrestrained

[a]Floor and roof systems can be considered restrained when they are tied into walls with or without tie beams, the walls being designed and detailed to resist thermal thrust from the floor or roof system.

[b]For example, resistance to potential thermal expansion is considered to be achieved when:

(1) Continuous structural concrete topping is used.

(2) The space between the ends of precast units or between the ends of units and the vertical face of supports is filled with concrete or mortar.

(3) The space between the ends of precast units and the vertical faces of supports, or between the ends of solid or hollow core slab units does not exceed 0.25 percent of the length for normal weight concrete members or 0.1 percent of the length for structural lightweight concrete members.

Fig. 6.4.3. Typical examples of restrained floors or roofs of precast construction

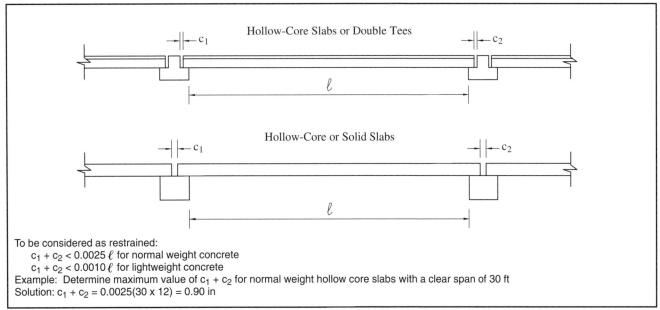

To be considered as restrained:
$c_1 + c_2 < 0.0025\,\ell$ for normal weight concrete
$c_1 + c_2 < 0.0010\,\ell$ for lightweight concrete
Example: Determine maximum value of $c_1 + c_2$ for normal weight hollow core slabs with a clear span of 30 ft
Solution: $c_1 + c_2 = 0.0025(30 \times 12) = 0.90$ in

Example 6.4.1

Hollow core floor slabs were installed in a building several years ago when a 1 hr. fire endurance was required. The occupancy of the building will be changed and the floors must qualify for a 3 hr. fire endurance. What can be done to upgrade the fire endurance?

Given:

Slabs are 4 ft wide, 8 in deep, prestressed with five $^3/_8$ in 270 ksi strands located 1 in above the bottom of the slab, and span 24 ft. Slabs are made with 5000 psi siliceous aggregate concrete, have an equivalent thickness of 3.75 in, and weigh 47 psf. The slabs are untopped and the superimposed load will be 50 psf.

Solution:

There are a number of possible solutions. The appropriate solution will depend on architectural or functional requirements and economics.

For some parts of the building, the slabs might be made to qualify as "restrained" in accordance with Figure 6.4.2 and Figure 6.4.3, in which case those slabs would qualify structurally for 3 hours, but would still have to be upgraded to qualify for 3 hours by heat transmission.

A gypsum wallboard ceiling installed as shown in Figure 6.2.3 would provide three hours both structurally and for heat transmission. Calculations of the ultimate capacity and stresses should be made to assure that the added weight of the ceiling can be adequately supported.

A spray-applied undercoating of vermiculite cementitious material or sprayed mineral fiber can also be used. For heat transmission, the required thickness for three hours of undercoating is 0.6 in (see Figure 6.2.2.1). From Figure 6.3.2, it can be seen that with a thickness of 0.6 in of VCM or SMF, the equivalent thickness of concrete cover is more than 2 in. Thus, the equivalent "u" distance is more than 2 in plus 1 in or more than 3 in. From Figure 6.3.1.4, with u more than 3 in, the strand temperature will be less than 600 degrees F at three hours, so the strength of the prestressing steel will be 65% of its 70 degrees F strength (Figure 6.3.1.5) or more than 0.65 x 270 = 175.5 ksi. Calculations can be made in accordance with the procedures in the section headed "Simply Supported Slabs", but if the strand strength is reduced less than about 50% of its room temperature strength, the assembly will generally be satisfactory structurally.

CHAPTER 7

ACOUSTICAL PROPERTIES OF
HOLLOW CORE FLOOR SLABS

7.1 Glossary

Airborne Sound - sound that reaches the point of interest by propagation through air.

Background Level - the ambient sound pressure level existing in a space.

Decibel (dB) - a logarithmic unit of measure of sound pressure or sound power. Zero on the decibel scale corresponds to a standardized references pressure (20 μPa) or sound power (10^{-12} watt).

Flanking Transmission - transmission of sound by indirect paths other than through the primary barrier.

Frequency (Hz) - the number of complete vibration cycles per second.

Impact Insulation Class (IIC) - a single figure rating of the overall impact sound insulation merits of floor-ceiling assemblies in terms of a reference contour (ASTM E989).

Impact Noise - the sound produced by one object striking another.

Noise - unwanted sound.

Noise Criteria (NC) - a series of curves, used as design goals to specify satisfactory background sound levels as they relate to particular use functions.

Noise Reduction (NR) - the difference in decibels between the space-time average sound pressure levels produced in two enclosed spaces by one or more sound sources in one of them.

Noise Reduction Coefficient (NRC) - the arithmetic average of the sound absorption coefficients at 250, 500, 1000 and 2000 Hz expressed to the nearest multiple of 0.05 (ASTM C423).

Reverberation - the persistence of sound in an enclosed or partially enclosed space after the source of sound has stopped.

Room Criteria (RC) Curves - a revision of the NC curves based on empirical studies of background sounds.

Sabin - the unit of measure of sound absorption (ASTM C423).

Sound Absorption Coefficient (α) - the fraction of randomly incident sound energy absorbed or otherwise not reflected off a surface (ASTM C423).

Sound Pressure Level (SPL) - ten times the common logarithm of the ratio of the square of the sound pressure to the square of the standard reference pressure of 20 μPa. Commonly measured with a sound level meter and microphone, this quantity is expressed in decibels.

Sound Transmission Class (STC) - the single number rating system used to give a preliminary estimate of the sound insulation properties of a partition system. This rating is derived from measured values of transmission loss (ASTM E413).

Sound Transmission Loss (TL) - ten times the common logarithm of the ratio, expressed in decibels, of the airborne sound power incident on the partition that is transmitted by the partition and radiated on the other side (ASTM E90).

Structureborne Sound - sound that reaches the point of interest over at least part of its path by vibration of a solid structure.

7.2 General

The basic purpose of architectural acoustics is to provide a satisfactory environment in which desired sounds are clearly heard by the intended listeners and unwanted sounds (noise) are isolated or absorbed.

Under most conditions, the architect/ engineer can determine the acoustical needs of the space and then design the building to satisfy those needs. Good acoustical design utilizes both absorptive and reflective surfaces, sound barriers and vibration isolators. Some surfaces must reflect sound so that the loudness will be adequate in all areas where listeners are located. Other surfaces absorb sound to avoid echoes, sound distortion and long reverberation times. Sound is isolated from rooms where it is not wanted by selected wall and floor-ceiling constructions. Vibration generated by mechanical equipment must be isolated from the structural frame of the building.

Most acoustical situations can be described in terms of: (1) sound source, (2) sound transmission path, and (3) sound receiver. Sometimes the source strength and path can be controlled and the receiver made more attentive by removing distraction or made more tolerant of disturbance. Acoustical design must include consideration of these three elements.

7.3 Approaching the Design Process

Criteria must be established before the acoustical design of a building can begin. Basically a satisfactory acoustical environment is one in which the character and magnitude of all sounds are compatible with the intended space function.

Although a reasonable objective, it is not always easy to express these intentions in quantitative terms. In addition to the amplitude of sound, the properties such as spectral characteristics, continuity, reverberation and intelligibility must be specified.

People are highly adaptable to the sensations of heat, light, odor, sound, etc. with sensitivities varying widely. The human ear can detect a sound intensity of rustling leaves, 10 dB, and can tolerate, if even briefly, the powerful exhaust of a jet engine at 120 dB, 10^{12} times the intensity of the rustling sound.

7.3.1 Dealing with Sound Levels

The problems of sound insulation are usually considerably more complicated than those of sound absorption. The former involves reductions of sound level, which are of the greater orders of magnitude than can be achieved by absorption. These reductions of sound level from space to space can be achieved only by continuous, impervious barriers. If the problem also involves structure borne sound, it may be necessary to introduce resilient layers or discontinuities into the barrier.

Sound absorbing materials and sound insulating materials are used for different purposes. There is not much sound absorption from an 8 in (200 mm) hollow core concrete slab; similarly, high sound insulation is not available from a porous lightweight material that may be applied to room surfaces. It is important to recognize that the basic mechanisms of sound absorption and sound insulation are quite different.

7.4 Sound Transmission Loss

Sound transmission loss measurements are made at 16 frequencies at one-third octave intervals covering the range from 125 to 4000 Hz. The testing procedure is ASTM Specification E90, Laboratory Measurement of Airborne Sound Transmission Loss of Building Partitions. To simplify specification of desired performance characteristics, the single number Sound Transmission Class (STC) was developed.

Airborne sound reaching a floor or ceiling produces vibration in the slab and is radiated with reduced intensity on the other side. Airborne sound transmission loss of a floor-ceiling assembly is a function of its weight, stiffness and vibration damping characteristics.

Weight is concrete's greatest asset when it is used as a sound insulator. For sections of similar design, but different weights, the STC increases approximately 6 units for each doubling of weight as shown in Figure 7.4.1.

Fig. 7.4.1 Sound Transmission Class as a function of weight of floor

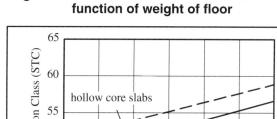

Fig. 7.4.2 Acoustical test data of hollow core slabs (normal weight concrete)

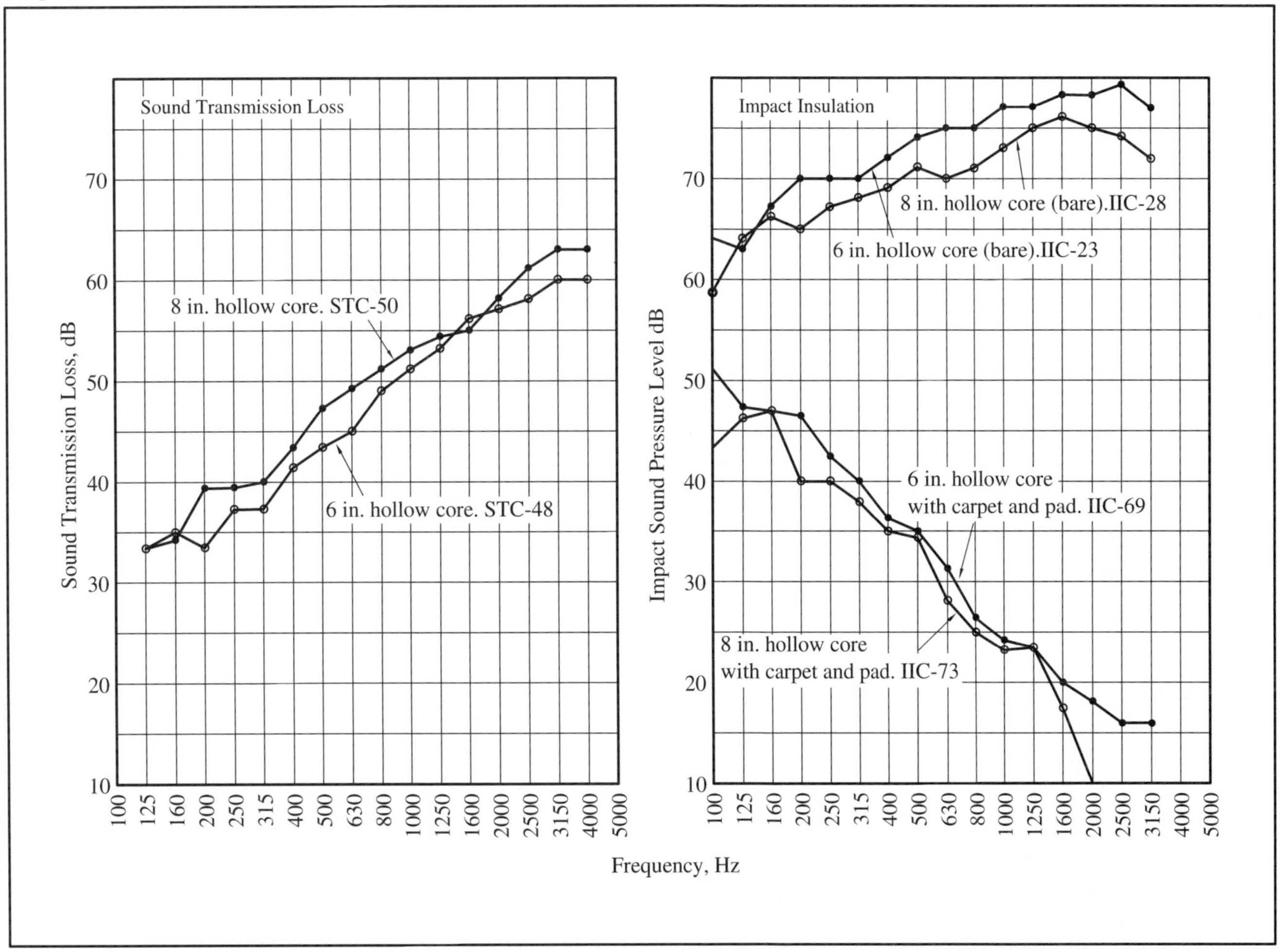

Precast concrete floors and roofs usually do not need additional treatments in order to provide adequate sound insulation. If desired, greater sound insulation can be obtained by using a resiliently attached layer(s) of gypsum board or other building material. The increased transmission loss occurs because the energy flow path is now increased to include a dissipative air column and additional mass.

The acoustical test results of both airborne sound transmission loss and impact insulation of 6 and 8 in (150 and 200 mm) hollow core slabs are shown in Figure 7.4.2. Table 7.4.1 presents the ratings for various floor-ceiling assemblies.

7.5 Impact Noise Reduction

Footsteps, dragged chairs, dropped objects, slammed doors, and plumbing generate impact noise. Even when airborne sounds are adequately controlled there can be severe impact noise problems.

The test method used to evaluate systems for impact sound insulation is described in ASTM Specification E492, Laboratory Measurement of Impact Sound Transmission Using the Tapping Machine. As with the airborne standard, measurements are made at 16 one-third octave intervals but in the range from 100 to 3150 Hz. For performance specification purposes, the single number Impact Insulation Class (IIC) is used.

Hollow core floors in combination with resilient materials effectively control impact sound. One simple solution consists of good carpeting on resilient padding. Table 7.4.1 shows that a carpet and pad over a bare slab will significantly increase the impact noise reduction. The overall efficiency varies according to the characteristics of the carpeting and padding such as resilience, thickness and weight. So called resilient flooring materials, such as linoleum, rubber, asphalt vinyl, etc. are not entirely satisfactory directly on concrete, nor are parquet or strip wood floors when applied directly. Impact sound also may be controlled by

Table 7.4.1 Airborne sound transmission and impact insulation class ratings from laboratory tests of hollow core slab floor-ceiling assemblies

Assembly No.	Description	STC	IIC
1.	6 in (150 mm) hollow core slabs	48	23
2.	Assembly 1 with carpet and pad	48	69
3.	Assembly 1 with $^1/_2$ in (13 mm) wood block flooring adhered directly	48	48
4.	Assembly 1 with $^1/_2$ in (13 mm) wood block flooring adhered to $^1/_2$ in (13 mm) sound-deadening board underlayment adhered to concrete	49	49
5.	Assembly 1 with $^3/_4$ in (19 mm) gypsum concrete	50	41
6.	Assembly 1 with $^3/_4$ in (19 mm) gypsum concrete on $^1/_2$ in (13 mm) sound-deadening board underlayment adhered to concrete	50	50
7.	Assembly 1 with carpet and pad on $^3/_4$ in (19 mm) gypsum concrete on $^1/_2$ in (13 mm) sound-deadening board underlayment adhered to concrete	50	72
8.	8 in (200 mm) hollow core slabs	50	28
9.	Assembly 8 with carpet and pad	50	73
10.	Assembly 8 with $^1/_2$ in (13 mm) wood block flooring adhered directly	51	47
11.	Assembly 8 with $^1/_2$ in (13 mm) wood block flooring adhered to $^1/_2$ in (13 mm) sound-deadening board underlayment adhered to concrete	52	54
12.	Assembly 8 with $^1/_2$ in (13 mm) wood block flooring adhered to $^1/_2$ in (13 mm) plywood adhered to $^7/_{16}$ in (11 mm) sound-deadening board underlayment adhered to concrete	52	55
13.	Assembly 8 with $^5/_{16}$ in (8 mm) wood block flooring adhered to $^1/_4$ in (6 mm) polystyrene underlayment adhered to concrete	50	51
14.	Assembly 8 with vinyl tile adhered to $^1/_2$ in (13 mm) plywood adhered to $^7/_{16}$ in (11 mm) sound-deadening board underlayment adhered to concrete	50	55
15.	Assembly 8 with vinyl tile adhered to $^1/_4$ in (6 mm) inorganic felt supported cushion underlayment adhered to concrete	50	51
16.	Assembly 8 with vinyl tile adhered to $^1/_8$ in (3 mm) polyethylene foam underlayment adhered to concrete	50	58
17.	Assembly 8 with 1 $^1/_2$ in (38 mm) concrete topping with carpet and pad	50	76
18.	Assembly 8 with 1 $^1/_2$ in (38 mm) concrete topping with vinyl tile adhered to concrete	50	44
19.	Assembly 8 with 1 $^1/_2$ in (38 mm) concrete topping with vinyl tile adhered to $^3/_8$ in (9 mm) plywood adhered to $^1/_2$ in (13 mm) sound-deadening board adhered to concrete	52	55
20.	Assembly 8 with 1 $^1/_2$ in (38 mm) concrete with $^1/_2$ in (13 mm) wood block flooring adhered to $^1/_2$ in (13 mm) sound-deadening board adhered to concrete	51	53
21.	Assembly 8 with 1 $^1/_2$ in (38 mm) concrete with $^5/_{16}$ in (8 mm) wood block flooring adhered to foam backing adhered to concrete	51	54
22.	Assembly 8 with $^3/_4$ in (19 mm) gypsum concrete with $^5/_{16}$ in (8 mm) wood block flooring adhered to foam backing adhered to concrete	50	53
23.	Assembly 11 with acoustical ceiling	59	61
24.	Assembly 8 with quarry tile, 1 $^1/_4$ in (32 mm) reinforced mortar bed with 0.4 in (10 mm) nylon and carbon black spinerette matting	60	54
25.	Assembly 24 with suspended $^5/_8$ in (16 mm) gypsum board ceiling with 3 $^1/_2$ in (90 mm) insulation	61	62

providing a discontinuity in the structure such as would be obtained by adding a resilient-mounted plaster or drywall suspended ceiling.

7.6 Absorption of Sound

A sound wave always loses part of its energy as it is reflected by a surface. This loss of energy is termed sound absorption. It appears as a decrease in sound pressure of the reflected wave. The sound absorption coefficient is the fraction of energy incident but not reflected per unit of surface area. Sound absorption can be specified at individual frequencies or as an average of absorption coefficients (NRC).

A dense, non-porous concrete surface typically absorbs 1 to 2% of incident sound and has an NCR of 0.015. In the case where additional sound absorption of precast concrete is desired, a coating of acoustical material can be spray applied, acoustical tile can be applied with adhesive, or an acoustical ceiling can be suspended. Most of the spray applied fire retardant materials used to increase the fire resistance of precast concrete and other floor-ceiling systems can also be used to absorb sound. The NCR of the sprayed fiber types range from 0.25 to 0.75. Most cementitious types have an NCR from 0.25 to 0.50.

If an acoustical ceiling were added to Assembly 11 of Table 7.4.1 (as in Assembly 23), the sound entry through a floor or roof would be reduced 7dB. In addition, the acoustical ceiling would absorb a portion of the sound after entry and provide a few more decibels of quieting. Use of the following expression can be made to determine the intra-room noise or loudness reduction due to the absorption of sound.

$$NR = 10\log\frac{A_o + A_a}{A_a} \qquad \text{(Eq. 7.6.1)}$$

where

NR = sound pressure level reduction, dB

A_o = original absorption, Sabins

A_a = added absorption, Sabins

Values for A_o and A_a are the products of the absorption coefficients of the various room materials and their surface areas.

A plot of this equation is shown in Figure 7.6.1. For an absorption ratio of 5, the decibel reduction is 7dB. Note that the decibel reduction is the same, regardless of the original sound pressure level and depends only on the absorption ratio. This is due to the fact that the decibel scale is itself a scale of ratios, rather than difference in sound energy.

While a decibel difference is an engineering quantity which can be physically measured, it is also important to know how the ear judges the change in sound energy due to sound conditioning. Apart from the subjective annoyance factors associated with excessive sound reflection, the ear can make accurate judgments of the relative loudness between sounds. An approximate relation between percentage loudness, reduction of reflected sound and absorption ratio is plotted in Figure 7.6.2

The percentage loudness reduction does not depend on the original loudness, but only on the absorption ratio. (The curve is drawn for loudness within the normal range of hearing and does not apply to extremely faint sounds.) Referring again to the absorption ratio of 5, the loudness reduction is read from Figure 7.6.2 as approximately 40 percent.

7.7 Acceptable Noise Criteria

As a rule, a certain amount of continuous sound can be tolerated before it becomes noise. An "acceptable" level neither disturbs room occupants nor interferes with the communication of wanted sound.

The most widely accepted and used noise criteria today are expressed as the Noise Criterion (NC) curves, Figure 7.7.1a. The figures in Table 7.7.1 represent general acoustical goals. They can also be compared with anticipated noise levels in specific rooms to assist in evaluating noise reduction problems.

The main criticism of NC curves is that they are too permissive when the control of low or high frequency noise is of concern. For this reason, Room Criterion (RC) Curves were developed (Figure 7.7.1b).[39,40] RC curves are the result of extensive studies based on the human response to both sound pressure level and frequency and take into account the requirements for speech intelligibility.

A low background level obviously is necessary where listening and speech intelligibility is im-

Fig. 7.6.1 Relation of decibel reduction of reflected sound to absorption ratio

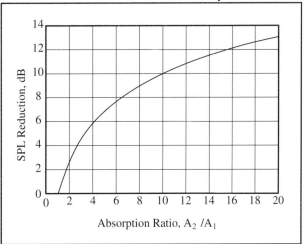

Fig. 7.6.2 Relation of percent loudness reduction of reflected sound to absorption ratio

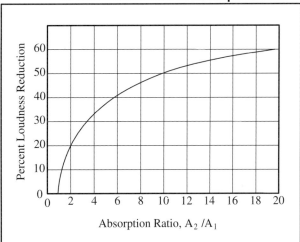

Fig. 7.7.1a NC (Noise Criteria) Curves

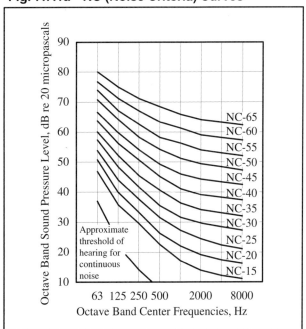

Fig. 7.7.1b RC (Room Criteria) Curves

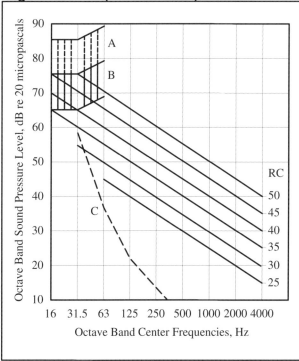

Region A: High probability that noise-induced vibration levels in lightweight wall/ceiling constructions will be clearly feelable; anticipate audible rattles in light fixtures, doors, windows, etc.
Region B: Noise-induced vibration levels in lightweight wall/ceiling constructions may be moderately feelable; slight possibility of rattles in light fixtures, doors, windows, etc.
Region C: Below threshold of hearing for continuous noise.

portant. Conversely, higher levels can persist in large business offices or factories where speech communication is limited to short distances. Often it is just as important to be interested in the minimum as in the maximum permissible levels of Table 7.7.1. In an office or residence, it is desirable to have a certain ambient sound level to assure adequate acoustical privacy between spaces, thus, minimizing the transmission loss requirements of unwanted sound (noise).

These undesirable sounds may be from an exterior source such as automobiles or aircraft, or they may be generated as speech in an adjacent classroom or music in an adjacent apartment. They may be direct impact-induced sound such as footfalls on the floor above, rain impact on a lightweight roof construction or vibrating mechanical equipment.

Thus, the designer must always be ready to accept the task of analyzing the many potential sources of intruding sound as related to their frequency characteristics and the rates at which they occur. The level of toleration that is to be expected by those who will occupy the space must also be established. Figures 7.7.2 and 7.7.3 are the spectral characteristics of common noise sources.

Fig. 7.7.2 Sound pressure levels - exterior noise sources

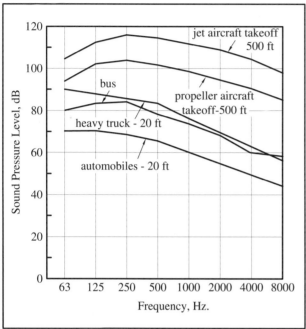

Fig. 7.7.3 Sound pressure levels - interior noise sources

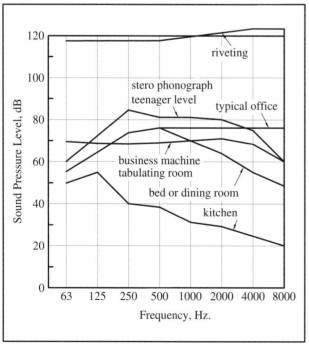

Table 7.7.1 Recommended category classification and suggested Noise Criteria range for steady background noise as heard in various in-door functional activity areas*[39]

TYPE OF SPACE	NC OR RC CURVE
1. Private residences	25 to 30
2. Apartments	30 to 35
3. Hotels/motels	
a. Individual rooms or suites	30 to 35
b. Meeting/banquet rooms	30 to 35
c. Halls, corridors, lobbies	35 to 40
d. Service/support areas	40 to 45
4. Offices	
a. Executive	25 to 30
b. Conference rooms	25 to 30
c. Private	30 to 35
d. Open-plan areas	35 to 40
e. Computer/business machine areas	40 to 45
f. Public circulation	40 to 45
5. Hospitals and clinics	
a. Private rooms	25 to 30
b. Wards	30 to 35
c. Operating rooms	25 to 30
d. Laboratories	30 to 35
e. Corridors	30 to 35
f. Public areas	35 to 40
6. Churches	25 to 30**
7. Schools	
a. Lecture and classrooms	25 to 30
b. Open-plan classrooms	30 to 35**
8. Libraries	30 to 35
9. Concert Halls	**
10. Legitimate theatres	**
11. Recording studios	**
12. Movie theatres	30 to 35

* Design goals can be increased by 5 dB when dictated by budget constraints or when noise intrusion from other sources represents a limiting condition.

**An acoustical expert should be consulted for guidance on these critical spaces.

Sound Pressure Level - (dB)								
Frequency (Hz)	63	125	250	500	1000	2000	4000	8000
Stereo Source Noise (teenager) (Figure 7.7.3)	60	72	84	82	82	80	75	60
Bedroom Room Criteria RC 30 (Figure 7.7.1)	50	45	40	35	30	25	20	15
Required Insulation	10	27	44	47	52	55	55	45

Sound Pressure Level - (dB)						
Frequency (Hz)	125	250	500	1000	2000	4000
Required Insulation	27	44	47	52	55	55
8 in H.C. (Figure 7.4.2)	34	39	46	53	59	64
Deficiencies	—	5	1	—	—	—

With these criteria, the problem of sound isolation now must be solved, namely, the reduction process between the high unwanted noise source and the desired ambient level. For this solution, two related yet mutually exclusive processes must be incorporated, i.e., sound transmission loss and sound absorption.

7.8 Establishment of Noise Insulation objectives

Often acoustical control is specified as to the minimum insulation values of the dividing partition system. Municipal building codes, lending institutions and the Department of Housing and Urban Development (HUD) list both airborne STC and impact IIC values for different living environments. For example, the HUD minimum property standards[41] are:

LOCATION	STC	IIC
Between living units	45	45
Between living units and public space	50	50

Once the objectives are established, the designer then should refer to available data, e.g., Fig. 7.4.2 or Table 7.4.1 and select the system which best meets these requirements. In this respect, concrete systems have superior properties and can, with minimal effort, comply with these criteria. When the insulation value has not been specified, selection of the necessary barrier can be de-termined analytically by (1) identifying exterior and/or interior noise sources, and (2) by establishing acceptable interior noise criteria.

Example 7.8.1

Assume a precast prestressed concrete apartment building with hollow core floor slabs. The first step is to determine the degree of acoustical insulation required of the floor-ceiling assembly by using Figures 7.4.1 and 7.7.3

The 500 Hz requirement, 47 dB, can be used as the first approximation of the floor STC category.

The selected floor should meet or exceed the insulation needs at 11 frequencies. However, to achieve the most efficient design conditions, certain limited deficiencies can be tolerated. Experience has shown that the maximum deficiencies are 3 dB on one frequency point.

7.9 Leaks and Flanking

The performance of a building section with an otherwise adequate STC can be seriously reduced by a relatively small hole or any other path which allows sound to bypass the acoustical barrier. All noise which reaches a space by paths other than through the primary barrier is called flanking. Common flanking paths are openings around doors or windows, at electrical outlets, telephone and television connections, and pipe and duct penetrations. Suspended ceilings in rooms where walls do not extend from the ceiling to the roof or floor above allow sound to travel to adjacent rooms.

Fig. 7.9.1 Effect of safing insulation seals

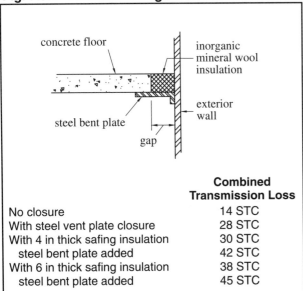

	Combined Transmission Loss
No closure	14 STC
With steel vent plate closure	28 STC
With 4 in thick safing insulation	30 STC
steel bent plate added	42 STC
With 6 in thick safing insulation	38 STC
steel bent plate added	45 STC

Anticipation and prevention of leaks begins at the design stage. Flanking paths (gaps) at the perimeters of interior precast walls and floors are generally sealed during construction with grout or drypack. In addition, all openings around penetrations through walls or floors should be as small as possible and must be sealed airtight. The higher the STC of the barrier, the greater the effect of an unsealed opening.

Perimeter leakage more commonly occurs at the intersection between an exterior curtain wall and floor slab. It is of vital importance to seal this gap in order to retain the acoustical integrity of the system as well as provide the required fire stop between floors. One way to achieve this seal is to place a 4 pcf (64 kg/m^3) density mineral wood blanket between the floor slab and the exterior wall. Figure 7.9.1 demonstrates the acoustical isolation effects of this treatment.

In exterior walls, the proper application of sealant and backup materials in the joints between units will not allow sound to flank the wall.

If the acoustical design is balanced, the maximum amount of acoustic energy reaching a space via flanking should not equal the energy transmitted through the primary barriers.

Although not easily quantified, an inverse relationship exists between the performance of an element as a primary barrier and its propensity to transmit flanking sound. In other words, the probability of existing flanking paths in a concrete structure is much less than in one of steel or wood frame.

In addition to using basic structural materials, flanking paths can be minimized by:

1. Interrupting the continuous flow of energy with dissimilar material, i.e., expansion or control joints or air gaps.

2. Increasing the resistance to energy flow with floating floor systems, full height and/or double partitions and suspended ceilings.

7.10 Human Response to Building Vibrations

Modern buildings often use components with low weight-to-strength ratios, which allow longer spans with less mass. This trend increasingly results in transient vibrations which are annoying to the occupants. Unlike equipment vibration, a person often causes the vibration and also senses it. These vibrations usually have very small amplitudes (less than 0.05 in [1 mm]) and were not noticed in older structures with heavier framing and more numerous and heavier partitions, which provided greater damping and other beneficial dynamic characteristics.

This problem is not well understood. Predicting human response to floor motion and the dynamic response to floor motion and the dynamic response of a floor system to moving loads are developing technologies. A number of discomfort criteria have been published[44-51], but they often give contradictory results.

The vibration problem is most effectively treated by modifying the structural system. The natural period (or its inverse, frequency), stiffness, mass, and damping are the structural parameters related to vibration control. Stiffness is increased by providing greater section properties than may be required for supporting loads. An increase in mass improves the natural frequency, but increases deflections and stresses, so by itself is only partially effective in controlling vibrations. For example, increasing the depth of a flexural member will aid greatly in vibration control, but increasing the width will not.

Recent research has emphasized the effect that damping plays in the human perception of vibration. In a study of 91 floor systems it was concluded that with damping greater than 5.5 to 6 percent of critical, structural systems were acceptable; systems with less were not[46]. Damping is usually attributed to the existence of partitions, supported mechanical work, ceilings and similar items, but is really not well understood. Guides for quantifying damping effect are scarce, and those that are available are very approximate[49-51].

7.11 Vibration Isolation for Mechanical Equipment

Vibration produced by equipment with unbalanced operating or starting forces can usually be isolated from the structure by mounting on a heavy concrete slab placed on resilient supports. This type of slab, called an inertia block, provides a low center of gravity to compensate for thrusts such as those generated by large fans.

For equipment with less unbalanced weight, a "housekeeping" slab is sometimes used below the resilient mounts to provide a rigid support for the mounts and to keep them above the floor so they are easier to clean and inspect. This slab may also be mounted on pads of precompressed glass fiber or neoprene.

The natural frequency of the total load on resilient mounts must be well below the frequency generated by the equipment. The required weight of an inertia block depends on the total weight of the machine and the unbalanced force. For a long stroke compressor, five to seven times its weight might be needed. For high pressure fans, one to five times the fan weight is usually sufficient.

A floor supporting resiliently mounted equipment must be much stiffer than the isolation system. If the static deflection of the floor approaches the static deflection of the mounts, the floor becomes a part of the vibrating system, and little vibration isolation is achieved. In general, the floor deflection should be limited to about 15 percent of the deflection of the mounts.

Simplified theory shows that for 90% vibration isolation, a single resilient supported mass (isolator) should have a natural frequency of about 1/3 the driving frequency of the equipment. The natural frequency of this mass can be calculated by:[52]

$$f_n = 188 \sqrt{1/\Delta_i} \qquad \text{(Eq. 7.11.1)}$$

where:

f_n = natural frequency of the isolator, CPM

Δ_i = static deflection of the isolator, in

From the above, the required static deflection of an isolator can be determined as follows:

$$f_n = f_d/3 = 188 \sqrt{1/\Delta_i} \text{ or}$$

$$\Delta_i = (564/f_d)^2 \qquad \text{(Eq. 7.11.2)}$$

and:

$$\Delta_f \leq 0.15 \, \Delta_i \qquad \text{(Eq. 7.11.3)}$$

where:

f_d = driving frequency of the equipment

Δ_f = static deflection of the floor system caused by the weight of the equipment, including inertia block, at the location of the equipment.

Example 7.11.1 - Vibration Isolation

Given:

A piece of mechanical equipment has a driving frequency of 800 CPM.

Problem:

Determine the approximate minimum deflection of the isolator and the maximum deflection of the floor system that should be allowed.

Solution:

Isolator, $\Delta_i = (564/800)^2 = 0.50$ in.
Floor, $\Delta_f = 0.15(0.50) = 0.07$ in.

Additional Bibliography
L.L. Beranek; *Noise Reduction*, McGraw-Hill Book Co., New York, 1960.

Ceramic Tile Institute of America and American Enka Company unpublished floor/ceiling tests.

C.M. Harris, *Handbook of Noise Control*, McGraw-Hill Book Co., New York, 1967.

C.M. Harris, C.E. Crede; *Shock & Vibration Handbook* - 2nd ed., McGraw-Hill Book Co., New York, 1976.

A. Litvin, H.W. Belliston; "Sound Transmission Loss Through Concrete and Concrete Masonry Walls", ACI Journal, December, 1978.

CHAPTER 8

GUIDE SPECIFICATION FOR PRECAST, PRESTRESSED HOLLOW CORE SLABS

This Guide Specification is intended to be used as a basis for the development of an office master specification or in the preparation of specifications for a particular project. In either case, this Guide Specification must be edited to fit the conditions of use.

Particular attention should be given to the deletion of inapplicable provisions. Necessary items related to a particular project should be included. Also, appropriate requirements should be added where blank spaces have been provided

The Guide Specifications are on the left. *Notes to Specifiers are on the right.*

GUIDE SPECIFICATIONS

1. GENERAL

1.01 Description

A. Work Included:

1. These specifications cover manufacture, transportation, and erection of precast, prestressed concrete hollow core slabs including grouting of joints between adjacent slab units.

B. Related Work Specified Elsewhere:
   1. Cast-in-Place Concrete: Section _____.

   2. Architectural Precast Concrete: Section _____.

   3. Precast Structural Concrete: Section _____.

   4. Structural Metal Framing: Section _____.

   5. Masonry Bearing Walls: Section _____.

   6. Underlayments: Section_____.

NOTES TO SPECIFIERS

1.01.A This Section is to be in Division 3 of Construction Specifications Institute format.

1.01.B.1 Includes structural or non-structural topping. See Section 2.5 for discussion of composite, structural topping.

1.01.B.3 Beams, columns, etc.
Prestressed concrete may be specified in Section _____.

1.01.B.4 Includes support framework not supplied by Hollow Core Slab Manufacturer.

1.01.B.5 Include any inserts or anchoring devices required for slab connections.

1.01.B.6 Underlayment may be any of the following general types: asphaltic concrete, gypsum concrete, latex concrete, mastic underlayment.

7. Caulking and Sealants: Section _____.

1.01.B.7 Caulking between slab edges at exposed underside of floor members and/or perimeter caulking may be included in this section.

8. Holes for Mechanical Equipment: Section _____.

1.01.B.8 Holes may be drilled or cut and trimmed with a chisel. Cut outline of hole through lower portion of slab from underside, after which the top side may be removed from above. Do not cut prestressing strand without permission of engineer.

9. Painting: Section _____.

1.01.B.9 Prime coat should be a latex base paint. Finish coat may be an oil base, flat wall or emulsified finish

10. Carpet and Pad: Section _____.

1.01.B.10 Specify minimum 55 oz. pad when no cast-in-place topping is used

11. Roofing and Roof Insulation: Section _____.

1.01.B.11 Non-absorbent rigid board insulation 1" or more in thickness should be used on roofs. Check local energy code for exact requirements.

1.02 Quality Assurance

A. The *precast concrete manufacturing plant* shall be certified by the Precast/Prestressed Concrete Institute (PCI) Plant Certification Program. Manufacturer shall be certified at the time of bidding in Category C2.

1.02.A Structural Precast Products must meet the requirements of PCI Manual, MNL-116.

In Canada, the manufacture, transportation and erection of precast prestressed hollow core slabs is governed by the Canadian Standards Association Standard A23.4-94, "Precast Concrete - Materials and Construction".

Assurance of plant capability to produce quality precast concrete products is set by the CSA Standard A23.4-94. This Standard forms the basis of a certification program which sets rigid capability criteria for precast manufacturers, their personnel and operations.

B. Erector Qualifications: Regularly engaged for at least _____ years in the erection of *precast structural concrete* similar to the requirements of this project.

1.02.B Usually 2 to 5 years.

C. Qualifications of Welders: In accordance with AWS D1.1.

1.02.C Qualified within the past year.

D. Testing: In general compliance with applicable provisions of Precast/Prestressed Concrete Institute MNL-116, Manual for Quality Control for Plants and Production of Precast Prestressed Concrete Products.

GUIDE SPECIFICATIONS

E. Requirements of Regulatory Agencies: All local codes plus the following specifications, standards and codes are a part of these specifications:
1. ACI 318-Building Code Requirements for Structural Concrete.
2. AWS D1.1-Structural Welding Code - Steel.
3. AWS D1.4-Structural Welding Code - Reinforcing Steel.
4. ASTM Specifications - As referred to in Part 2 - Products, of this Specification.

1.03 Submittals

A. Shop Drawings

1. Erection Drawings
   a. Plans locating and defining all hollow core slab units furnished by the manufacturer, with all openings larger than 10 in (250 mm) shown and located.
   b. Sections and details showing connections, edge conditions and support conditions of the hollow core slab units.
   c. All dead, live and other applicable loads used in the design.
   d. Estimated cambers.

2. Production Drawings
   a. Plan view of each hollow core slab unit type.
   b. Sections and details to indicate quantities, location and type of reinforcing steel and prestressing strands.
   c. Lifting and erection inserts.
   d. Dimensions and finishes.
   e. Prestress for strand and concrete strength.

NOTES TO SPECIFIERS

1.02.E Always include the specific year or edition of the specifications, codes and standards used in the design of the project and made part of the specifications. Fire safety and resistance requirements are specified in local or model codes. When required, fire rated products shall be clearly identified on the design drawings.

For projects in Canada, the National Building Code of Canada governs design. Canadian Standards Association Standards A23.3-94, "Design of Concrete Structures" and A23.4-94, "Precast Concrete - Materials and Construction" also apply. Fire resistance is specified in the National Building Code and the National Fire Code.

1.03.A.1.a Openings shown on erection drawings are considered in the slab design. Verify slab adequacy for any other openings with the Engineer of Record.

1.03.A.1.d Floor slabs receiving cast-in-place topping. The elevation of top of floor and amount of concrete topping must allow for camber of prestressed concrete members.

1.03.A.2 Production drawings are normally submitted only upon request.

f. Estimated camber at release.

g. Method of transportation.

B. Product Design Criteria
1. Loadings for design
a. Initial handling and erection stresses.
b. All dead and live loads as specified on the contract drawings
c. All other loads specified for hollow core slab units where applicable.
2. Design calculations of *products* not completed on the contract drawings shall be performed by a registered engineer experienced in *precast prestressed concrete design* and submitted for approval upon request.
3. Design shall be in accordance with ACI 318 or applicable codes.

C. Permissible Design Deviations
1. Design deviations will be permitted only after the Architect/Engineer's written approval of the manufacturer's proposed design supported by complete design calculations and drawings.
2. Design deviation shall provide an installation equivalent to the basic intent without incurring additional cost to the owner.

D. Test Report: Reports of tests on concrete and other materials upon request.

2. PRODUCTS

2.01 Materials

A. Portland Cement:
1. ASTM C150 - Type I or III

B. Admixtures:

1. Air-Entraining Admixtures: ASTM C260.
2. Water Reducing, Retarding, Accelerating, High Range Water Reducing Admixtures: ASTM C494.

C. Aggregates:
1. ASTM C33 or C330.

1.03 B and C Contract drawings normally will be prepared using a local precast prestressed concrete hollow core slab manufacturer's design data and load tables. Dimensional changes which would not materially affect architectural and structural properties or details usually are permissible.

Be sure that loads shown on the contract drawings are easily interpreted. For instance, on members which are to receive concrete topping, be sure to state whether all superimposed dead and live loads on precast prestressed members do or do not include the weight of the concrete topping. It is best to list the live load, superimposed dead load, topping weight, and weight of the member, all as separate loads. Where there are two different live loads (e.g., roof level of a parking structure) indicate how they are to be combined. Where additional structural support is required for openings, design headers in accordance with hollow core slab manufacturer's recommendations.

2.01 Delete or add materials that may be required for the particular job.

2.01.B Verify ability of local producer to use admixtures

D. Water:

Potable or free from foreign materials in amounts harmful to concrete and embedded steel.

E. Reinforcing Steel:
1. Bars:
Deformed Billet Steel: ASTM A615.
Deformed Rail Steel: ASTM A616.
Deformed Axle Steel: ASTM A617.
Deformed Low Alloy Steel: ASTM A706.
2. Wire:
Cold Drawn Steel: ASTM A82.

F. Prestressing Strand:
1. Uncoated, 7-Wire, Stress-Relieved Strand: ASTM A416 (including supplement) - Grade 250K or 270K.
2. Uncoated, Weldless 2- and 3-Wire Strand: ASTM A910
3. Indented, 7-Wire, Stress-Relieved Strand: ASTM A886 (including supplement)

G. Welded Studs: In accordance with AWS D1.1.

H. Structural Steel Plates and Shapes: ASTM A36.

I. Grout:
1. Cement grout: Grout shall be a mixture of not less than one part portland cement to three parts fine sand, and the consistency shall be such that joints can be completely filled but without seepage over adjacent surfaces. Any grout that seeps from the joint shall be completely removed before it hardens.

J. Bearing Strips:
1. Random Oriented Fiber Reinforced: Shall support a compressive stress of 3000 psi (20.7 MPa) with no cracking, splitting or delaminating in the internal portions of the pad. One specimen shall be tested for each 200 pads used in the project.

2.01.E.1 When welding of bars is required, weldability must be established to conform to AWS D1.4.

2.01.F Low-relaxation strand is the predominant strand in use. References to stress-relieved strand are from the ASTM titles.

2.01.H When required for anchorage or lateral bracing to structural steel members, some methods of manufacturing hollow core slabs preclude the use of anchors and inserts

2.01.I Grout strengths of 2000 psi to 3000 psi (13.8 - 20.7 MPa) can generally be achieved with the proportions noted. Rarely is higher strength grout required. Non-shrink grout is not required for satisfactory performance of hollow core slab systems.

2.01.J.1 Standard guide specifications are not available for random-oriented, fiber-reinforced pads. Proof testing of a sample from each group of 200 pads is suggested. Normal design working stresses are 1500 psi (10.3 MPa), so the 3000 psi (20.7 MPa) test load provides a factor of 2 over design stress. The shape factor for the test specimens should not be less than 2.

2. Plastic: Multi-monomer plastic strips shall be non-leaching and support construction loads with no visible overall expansion.

3. Tempered Hardboard.

4. Untempered Hardboard

2.02 Concrete Mixes

A. 28-day compressive strength: Minimum of ____ psi.

B. Release strength: Minimum of ____ psi.

C. Use of calcium chloride, chloride ions or other salts is not permitted.

2.03 Manufacture

A. Manufacturing procedures shall be in compliance with PCI MNL-116.

B. Manufacturing Tolerances: Manufacturing tolerances shall comply with PCI MNL-116.

C. Openings: Manufacturer shall provide for those openings 10 in (250 mm) round or square or larger as shown on the structural drawings. Other openings shall be located and field drilled or cut by the trade requiring them after the hollow core slab units have been erected. Openings and/or cutting of prestressing strand shall be approved by Architect/Engineer and manufacturer before drilling or cutting.

D. Patching: Will be acceptable providing the structural adequacy of the hollow core unit is not impaired.

3. EXECUTION

3.01 Product Deliver, Storage, and Handling

A. Delivery and Handling:

2.01.J.2 Plastic pads are widely used with hollow core slabs. Compression stress in use is not normally over a few hundred psi and proof testing is not considered necessary. No standard guide specifications are available.

2.01.J.3 Hardboard bearing strips should not be used in areas where undesirable staining is possible or where bearing strips may be continually wet.

2.02.A and B   Verify with local manufacturer. 5000 (35 MPa) psi for prestressed products is normal practice, with release strength of 3000 psi (20.7 MPa).

2.03.C   This paragraph requires other trades to field drill holes needed for their work, and such trades should be alerted to this requirement through proper notation in their sections of the specifications. Some manufacturers prefer to install openings smaller than 10 in (250 mm) which is acceptable if their locations are properly identified on the contract drawings

1. Hollow core slab units shall be lifted and supported during manufacturing, stockpiling, transporting and erection operations only at the lifting or supporting point, or both, as shown on the shop drawings, and with approved lifting devices. Lifting inserts shall have a minimum safety factor of 4. Exterior lifting hardware shall have a minimum safety factor of 5.

2. Transportation, site handling, and erection shall be performed with acceptable equipment and methods, and by qualified personnel.

B. Storage:

1. Store all units off ground.
2. Place stored units so that identification marks are discernible.
3. Separate stacked members by battens across full width of each slab unit.
4. Stack so that lifting devices are accessible and undamaged.
5. Do not use upper member of stacked tier as storage area for shorter member or heavy equipment.

3.02 Erection

A. Site Access: The General Contractor shall be responsible for providing suitable access to the building, proper drainage and firm level bearing for the hauling and erection equipment to operate under their own power.

B. Preparation: The General Contractor shall be responsible for:

1. Providing true, level bearing surfaces on all field placed bearing walls and other field placed supporting members.

2. All pipes, stacks, conduits and other such items shall be stubbed off at a level lower than the bearing plane of the prestressed concrete products until after the latter are set.

3.02.B Construction tolerances for cast-in-place concrete, masonry, etc., should be specified in those sections of the specifications.

3.02.B.2 Should be in Electrical, Mechanical, and Plumbing sections of project specifications.

C. Installation: Installation of hollow core slab units shall be performed by the manufacturer or a competent erector. Members shall be lifted by means of suitable lifting devices at points provided by the manufacturer. Bearing strips shall be set, where required. Temporary shoring and bracing, if necessary, shall comply with manufacturer's recommendations. Grout keys shall be filled.

D. At Slab Ends (where shown on Drawings): Provide suitable end cap or dam in voids as required.

E. For areas where slab voids are to be used as electrical raceways or mechanical ducts provide a taped butt joint at end of slabs, making sure the voids are aligned.

F. Alignment: Members shall be properly aligned and leveled as required by the approved shop drawings. Variations between adjacent members shall be reasonably leveled out by jacking, loading, or any other feasible method as recommended by the manufacturer and acceptable to the Architect/Engineer.

3.03 Field Welding

A. Field welding is to be done by qualified welders using equipment and materials compatible with the base material.

3.04 Attachments

A. Subject to approval of the Architect/Engineer, hollow core slab units may be drilled or "shot" provided no contact is made with the prestressing steel. Should spalling occur, it shall be repaired by the trade doing the drilling or the shooting.

3.05 Inspection and Acceptance

A. Final observation of erected hollow core slab units shall be made by Architect/Engineer for purposes of final payment.

3.02.D If a bearing wall building, special care must be taken. Delete when end grouting is not required.

3.02.E Delete when voids not used for electrical or mechanical.

3.02.F Tolerances should comply with industry tolerances published in "Tolerances for Precast and Prestressed Concrete", Prestressed Concrete Institute, JR307, 1985.[3]

REFERENCES

1. PCI Design Handbook - Precast and Pre-stressed Concrete, Fifth Edition, Precast/Prestressed Concrete Institute, Chicago, IL 1997.

2. ACI Committee 318, "Building Code Requirements for Structural Concrete (ACI 318-95) and Commentary (ACI 318R-95)", American Concrete Institute, Farmington Hills, MI, 1995.

3. PCI Committee on Tolerances, "Tolerances for Precast and Prestressed Concrete", PCI JOURNAL, Vol. 30, No. 1, January-February, 1985, pp. 26-112.

4. PCI Technical Activities Council, PCI Committee on Building Code, "PCI Standard Design Practice," PCI JOURNAL, V. 42, No. 2, March-April 1997, pp 34-51.

5. Zia, Paul, Preston, H. Kent, Scott, Norman L, and Workman, Edwin B., "Estimating Prestress Losses", Concrete International, June, 1979, pp 32-38.

6. Martin, L.D., "A Rational Method for Estimating Camber and Deflection of Precast, Prestressed Concrete Members", PCI JOURNAL, January-February, 1977.

7. ACI Committee 301, "Standard Specifications for Structural Concrete (ACI 301-96)", American Concrete Institute, Farmington Hills, MI, 1996.

8. Scott, Norman L., "Performance of Precast, Prestressed Hollow Core Slab with Composite Concrete Topping", PCI JOURNAL, March-April, 1973, pp 64-77.

9. Martin, Leslie D. and Scott, Norman L., "Development of Prestressing Strand in Pretensioned Members", ACI Journal, August 1976, pp 453-456.

10. Anderson, Arthur R., and Anderson, Richard G., "An Assurance Criterion for Flexural Bond in Pretensioned Hollow Core Units", ACI Journal, August, 1976, pp 457-464.

11. Discussion and Closure, "Development of Prestressing Strand in Pretensioned Members", ACI Journal, March, 1977, pp 136-137.

12. Discussion and Closure, "An Assurance Criterion for Flexural Bond in Pretensioned Hollow Core Units", ACI Journal, March, 1977, pp 137-140.

13. Zia, Paul and Mostafa, Talat, "Development Length of Prestressing Strands", PCI JOURNAL, September-October, 1977, pp 54-65.

14. Discussion and Closure, "Development Length of Prestressing Strands", PCI JOURNAL, July-August, 1978, pp 97-107.

15. Buckner, C. Dale, "A Review of Strand Development Length for Pretensioned Concrete Members", PCI JOURNAL, V. 40, No. 2, March-April, 1995, pp 84-105.

16. Discussion and Closure, "A Review of Strand Development Length for Pretensioned Concrete Members", PCI JOURNAL, V. 41, No. 2, March-April, 1996, pp 112-116.

17. Martin, Leslie D. and Korkosz, Walter J., "Strength of Prestressed Concrete Members at Sections Where Strands are not Fully Developed", PCI JOURNAL, V. 40, No. 5, September-October, 1995, pp 58-66.

18. Brooks, Mark D., Gerstle, Kurt H., and Logan, Donald R., "Effective of Initial Strand Slip on the Strength of Hollow Core Slabs", PCI JOURNAL, V. 33, No. 1, January-February, 1988, pp 90-111.

19. LaGue, David J., "Load Distribution Tests on Precast Prestressed Hollow Core Slab Construction", PCI JOURNAL, November-December, 1971, pp 10-18.

20. Van Acker, A., "Transversal Distribution of Linear Loadings in Prestressed Hollow Core Floors", BMA/MKT 84/006, September, 1983.

21. Johnson, Ted and Ghadiali, Zohair, "Load Distribution Test on Precast Hollow Core

Slabs with Openings", PCI JOURNAL, September-October, 1972, pp 9-19.

22. Pfeifer, Donald W. and Nelson, Theodore A., "Tests to Determine the Lateral Distribution of Vertical Loads in a Long-Span Hollow Core Floor Assembly", PCI JOURNAL, Vol. 28, No. 6, November-December, 1983, pp. 42-57.

23. Aswad, Alex and Jacques, Francis J., "Behavior of Hollow Core Slabs Subject to Edge Loads", PCI JOURNAL, V. 37, No. 2, March-April, 1992, pp 72-83.

24. Stanton, John F., "Response of Hollow Core Slab Floors to Concentrated Loads", PCI JOURNAL, V. 37, No. 4, July-August, 1992, pp 98-113.

25. Stanton, John F., "Proposed Design Rules for Load Distribution in Precast Concrete Decks", ACI Structural Journal, V. 84, No. 5, September-October, 1987, pp 371-382.

26. Rosenthal, I., "Full Scale Test of Continuous Prestressed Hollow Core Slab", PCI JOURNAL, Vol. 23, No. 3, May-June, 1978, pp. 74-81.

27. Harris, Harry G., and Iyengar, Srikanth, "Full Scale Tests on Horizontal Joints of Large Panel Precast Concrete Buildings", PCI JOURNAL, Vol 25, No. 2, March-April, 1980, pp. 72-92.

28. Johal, L.S. and Hanson, N.W., "Design for Vertical Load on Horizontal Connections in Large Panel Structures", PCI JOURNAL, Vol. 27, No. 1, January-February, 1982, pp 62-79.

29. PCI Committee on Precast Bearing Wall Buildings, "Considerations for the Design of Precast Concrete Bearing Wall Buildings to Withstand Abnormal Loads", PCI JOURNAL, Vol. 21, No. 2., March-April, 1976, pp. 18-51.

30. Fintel, Mark and Schultz, Donald M., "A Philosophy for Structural Integrity of Large Panel Buildings", PCI JOURNAL, Vol. 21, No. 3, May-June, 1976, pp. 46-69.

31. PCI Manual for Structural Design of Architectural Precast Concrete, PCI MNL-121-77, Prestressed Concrete Institute, Chicago, 1977.

32. Uniform Building Code, "Structural Engineering Design Provisions", V. 2, International Conference of Building Officials, Whittier, CA, 1994.

33. The BOCA® National Building Code, Thirteenth Edition, Building Officials & Code Administrators International, Inc., Country Club Hills, IL, 1996.

34. Cosper, Steven J., Anderson, Arthur R., Jobse, Harold J., "Shear Diaphragm Capacity of Untopped Hollow Core Floor Systems", Concrete Technology Associates, Technical Bulletin 80B3, 1981.

35. Clough, D.P., "Design of Connections for Precast Prestressed Concrete Buildings for the Effects of Earthquake", National Science Foundation, 1985.

36. Moustafa, Saad E., "Effectiveness of Shear-Friction Reinforcement in Shear Diaphragm Capacity of Hollow Core Slabs", PCI JOURNAL, Vol. 26, No. 1, January-February, 1981, pp 118-132.

37. Design and Detailing of Untopped Hollow Core Slab Systems for Diaphragm Shears, Structural Engineer's Association of Arizona, 1981/82.

38. PCI Fire Committee, "Design for Fire Resistance of Precast Prestressed Concreter-Second Edition", Precast/Prestressed Concrete Institute, Chicago, IL, 1989.

39. ASHRAE: ASHRAE Systems Handbook for 1984. American Society of Heating, Refrigerating & Air Conditioning Engineers, Inc., New York, 1984.

40. Blazier, W.E., "Revised Noise Criteria for Design and Rating of HVAC Systems", paper presented at ASHRAE Semiannual Meeting, Chicago, IL, January 26, 1981.

41. Berendt, R.D., Winzer, G.E., Burroughs, C.B.; "A Guide to Airborne, Impact and

Structureborne Noise Control in Multi-family Dwellings", prepared for Federal Housing Administration, U.S. Government Printing Office, Washington, D.C., 1975.

42. Sabine, H.J., Lacher, M.B., Flynn, D.R., Quindry, T.L.; "Acoustical and Thermal Performance of Exterior Residential Walls, Doors & Windows", National Bureau of Standards, U.S. Government Printing Office, Washington D.C., 1975.

43. IITRI; "Compendium of Materials for Noise Control", U.S. Department of Health, Education & Welfare, U.S. Government Printing Office, Washington, D.C., 1980.

44. "Vibrations of Concrete Structures", Publication SP-60, American Concrete Institute, Detroit, MI.

45. Galambos, T.V., Gould, P.C., Ravindra, M.R., Surgoutomo, H., and Crist, R.A., "Structural Deflections - A Literature and State-of-the-Art Survey", Building Science Series, Oct., 1973, National Bureau of Standards, Washington, D.C.

46. Murray, T.M., "Acceptability Criterion for Occupant-Induced Floor Vibration", Sound and Vibration, November, 1979.

47. "Design and Evaluation of Operation Breakthrough Housing Systems", NBS Report 10200, Amendment 4, September, 1970, U.S. Department of Housing and Urban Development, Washington, D.C.

48. Wiss, J.F. and Parmelee, R.H., "Human Perception of Transient Vibrations", Journal of the Structural Division, ASCE, Vol. 100, No. ST4, April, 1974.

49. "Guide to Floor Vibrations", *Steel Structures for Buildings-Limit States Design* CSA S16.1-1974, Appendix G. Canadian Standards Association, Rexdale, Ontario.

50. "Guide for the Evaluation of Human Exposure to Whole-Body Vibration", International Standard 2631, International Organization for Standardization, 1974.

51. Murray, T.M., "Design to Prevent Floor Vibration", Engineering Journal, AISC, Third Quarter, 1975.

52. Harris, C.M. and Crede, C.E., *Shock and Vibration Handbook*, 2nd Edition, McGraw-Hill, New York, NY, 1976.

INDEX